USES OF THE SEAS

 The American Assembly, *Columbia University*

USES OF THE SEAS

Prentice-Hall, Inc., *Englewood Cliffs, N.J.*
A SPECTRUM BOOK

Current printing (last number):

10 9 8 7 6 5 4 3 2 1

PRENTICE-HALL INTERNATIONAL, INC. (*London*)

Preface

This volume sets forth the new discoveries in oceanography and their implications for national and international law and organization; it also explores the implications of new shifts in the distribution of sea power among nations for international stability and for American policy.

Designed by its editor, Edmund A. Gullion, Dean of the Fletcher School of Law and Diplomacy of Tufts University, as a background volume for all American Assemblies on *Uses of the Seas* as well as for the general reader, the volume was first used by participants in the Thirty-third American Assembly at Arden House, Harriman, New York, May 2–5, 1968. The report of policy recommendations of that Assembly may be had as a separate pamphlet from The American Assembly.

The views contained herein are those of the writers and not necessarily of The American Assembly, a non-partisan educational organization which takes no position on matters it presents for public discussion. Similarly The Ford Foundation, which generously supported the entire American Assembly program on the seas, is not to be associated with the opinions expressed in the chapters which follow.

Clifford C. Nelson
President
The American Assembly

Table of Contents

Tables and Figures

Julius A. Stratton

Foreword

My childhood was spent on the northwest coast of our country. As a boy I listened spellbound to tales of ocean adventure—stories of a grandfather who had made his way through the Straits of Magellan to homestead in Oregon, of family enterprise in search of furs in the Bering Sea, of ninety-day passages to Sydney, and of shipwrecks off the shores of Alaska. And so at an early age I came to understand something of both the romance and the uses of the seas.

Among those youthful recollections, one in particular comes vividly to mind. It is that of a partially abandoned harbor, not far from where I lived, on Puget Sound. There, riding at anchor, rising and falling with the tide, lay a dozen or more three- and four-masted sailing vessels. Clipper ships, square-riggers—windjammers, as we called them—that had once plied the seven seas to and fro, bearing the commerce of the United States to Canton, to Calcutta, to Australia, and around the Horn to Europe and the Mediterranean. Now their spars and decks were bare. They would sail no more. In symbol and in fact they represented the end of an era. For countless centuries the development of trade, the exploration of distant lands, the spread of empire were all shaped and driven by the power of sail. Then came the new technologies of iron and steel and steam, and the great sailing fleets of history were outmoded and disappeared from the seas.

For a time the new style of the sea prospered. The first half of this century witnessed an extraordinary development of ocean liners, of enormous freighters, of dreadnoughts and destroyers and submarines.

Formerly president of Massachusetts Institute of Technology, JULIUS A. STRATTON *is chairman of the President's Commission on Marine Science, Engineering and Resources, and chairman of The Ford Foundation.*

But the pace of change quickened. Just as steam challenged the sail, so the advancing technology of the airplane has challenged and outstripped much of our ocean transport. The heavy battleship, which once commanded the seas, has been rendered obsolete; the strategic role of navies everywhere has been profoundly altered; and only lately we have seen the magnificent *Queen Mary* ignominiously retired to serve as a dockside tourist attraction.

Yet in the very moment that we are observing the demise of one epoch, a new one is in the making. There can hardly be a shadow of doubt that a wholly new era in the use of the seas lies immediately before us. New materials of construction, new means of propulsion, new instruments of observation, of navigation, and of communication will very shortly make it possible for man to explore and exploit the furthest depths of the ocean. And we may be assured that legitimate hopes of political advantage, of economic gain, or of the simple, basic desire to see and to know will take him there.

In our age—and very likely throughout all history—an advancing technology is the major instrument of cultural change. But change alone—change in man's capacity to construct and to destroy—is by no means of itself a guarantee of social progress, as we are learning to our dismay. The engineering triumphs of our time testify to what man *can* do. But what man will really have accomplished a generation hence, whether the product of extraordinary technical achievement will indeed be a better world, hangs in the balance. We shall tip those scales only by forethought, by analysis and understanding of the manifold implications of our expanding technology, by wise planning, and, above all, through the will to use our material power to rational purpose.

One of the most encouraging manifestations of hope and progress in these troubled times is the growing evidence of efforts to project into the future, to weigh consequences, to define options in areas of transcendent public import. There is no better example than the current endeavor to formulate a considered plan for the further development of our marine resources.

The future course of ocean science and technology is now relatively easy to foretell. But the economic, political, and social implications of these projected developments are infinitely complex. We have yet to learn the ultimate economic potential of the sea bottom. We have yet to exploit the ocean as a source of food for hungry people. We have yet to learn how to halt the pollution of our coastal waters. As we move down the continental slope and out along the deepest ocean floor, a multitude of questions arise that cannot wait too long for an answer. Where now are the limits of sovereignty? What regime shall we propose to assure the rights of exploration and to encourage and protect the investor? How shall we make of the oceans a domain for international collaboration rather than an arena for conflict? And what prudent steps must our own Navy take to guard the security of our country? Above all, how do we mobilize the resources of industry, of finance, and of government to take advantage rapidly and effectively of the vast promise of our new technology?

There lie before us countless problems to resolve, but the prospects for true progress are such as to excite the imagination of all those who care about the sea and who share a concern for its proper use. Over the past several years these prospects have stimulated both discussion and action at the national level. It was a concern for goals and concrete programs that led the Congress and the President to establish the Commission on Marine Science, Engineering and Resources, charged with the task of charting a national course for the years ahead.

The care with which we as a nation plot that course and the effectiveness with which we pursue it over the coming decades will affect not only the people of our own country but those of all the world as well. And so it is both fortunate and singularly appropriate that The American Assembly—founded for the express purpose of illuminating vital issues of national policy—should provide a common forum where the diverse, interlocking, and sometimes conflicting views of a complex modern society can be brought to focus on the uses of the seas.

USES OF THE SEAS

Edmund A. Gullion, Editor

Introduction:
New Horizons at Sea

> "Or like stout Cortez, when with eagle eyes,
> He stared at the Pacific—and all his men
> Look'd at each other with a wild surmise—
> Silent upon a peak in Darien."
>
> —*On First Looking into Chapman's Homer,*
> John Keats

More than four hundred and fifty years after Balboa (not Cortez), ranging ahead of his men, crested a rise in Panama and first beheld the Pacific Ocean, men gaze again upon the sea, their old familiar, with new surmise.

Always a changeable companion, the sea offers dramatic new horizons to the sailor and to the shore-bound, to the statesman and to the strategist, to the economist and to the lawyer, to the miner and the fisherman, to the old seafaring nations and to the newcomers among the hundred-odd states which border the oceans that still cover two-thirds of the earth's surface, but which are being radically foreshortened and shallowed by new technologies.

Man turns increasingly to the oceans for sustenance and security on

EDMUND A. GULLION *is dean of the Fletcher School of Law and Diplomacy, Tufts University. He served in the United States Foreign Service from 1937 to 1964, and has been ambassador to the Republic of Congo, senior foreign service inspector, and acting chief of the United States Disarmament Administration. He is a former member of the Policy Planning Staff of the State Department.*

a scale commensurate with the expansion of his needs, and the growth in his technical ability to use the seas. New questions, new problems, new opportunities are emerging.

At the same time that man's unending quest for food and treasure reaches for the deep waters, the security of the surface is being affected by shifts in the naval dispositions and the relative strength of the great naval powers. This volume is about both the peaceful and the military uses of the seas.

Science and Technology

Ocean technology has reached no plateau; if anything, the pace of change is accelerating. The result, so characteristic of this age, is that we must be as much or more concerned with predicting the technology of tomorrow and its imperatives for policy as we are with managing existing technology. Given our imperfect success with today's technology, the task before us is formidable.

In the field of peaceful uses, the primary interest, at least through 1980, will be in the recovery of both organic and mineral resources from the sea. Professor Paul Fye and his associates at the Woods Hole Oceanographic Institution sketch the prospects in Chapter 1.

The exciting prospects from an economic point of view are in the recovery of oil and gas. By 1964, one-sixth of the total production of oil and gas already came from offshore wells. The U.S. production of offshore oil in 1964 was worth $800 million; two years later it had risen to $1.1 billion. Oil is already being produced in water as deep as 285 feet. In 1967, an oil platform rig was completed off the Netherlands coast which can drill to 15,000 feet while resting on the bottom in 135 feet of water or afloat in 600 feet. The trend is bound to continue, especially as deep-water drilling technology continues to advance. The largest oil reserves may well be found not under the continental shelf adjacent to the coast, but on the continental slope or rise which is at ocean depths ranging to well below 3,000 meters. Deep drilling with robots and deep saturation diving will eventually permit these depths to be worked.

The potential for recovery of other non-living resources, organic, chemical, and mineral, is not as spectacular, but some exploitation is already being carried out and other possibilities loom ahead. For example, sea bed mining for phosphorites and manganese is a good prospect and imaginative engineers have seriously proposed to drill for manganese nodules in water as deep as 4,000 feet. Manganese may even be accreting on the sea floor at a rate greater than it is being mined on land (6 million tons per year). Nevertheless the land reserves are presently adequate. An extensive effort at sea would be warranted only if the United States chose to subsidize ocean recovery in order to reduce its dependence on foreign supplies.

In the field of precious metals, the sea is not yet the El Dorado of fable. The recovery of prosaic sand and gravel close to the coasts is substantial; but, contrary to vision and even to some report, the recovery of gold, platinum, tin or diamonds is not economically attractive for the foreseeable future. Still, the picture may change as new technologies emerge from the laboratory and put to sea.

Divers and deep sea stations will operate at ever greater depths. And a new race of mechanical deep sea monsters is coming into being to help man in his conquest of the deep. In 1966 and 1967, their real exploits earned the respectful interest of a public already bemused by their weird crustacean shapes. A "deep sea vehicle" capable of submergence to 6,000 feet located the hydrogen bomb jettisoned at sea off Palomares, Spain, in January, 1966, by a stricken U.S. strategic bomber. In 1967 the "Aluminaut" explored for minerals off the U.S. Atlantic coast at depths of 6,000 to 9,000 feet.

The tragedy of the loss in May, 1968, of the nuclear-powered submarine "Scorpion" and all within her brought agonized recognition that more funds and higher priorities might have provided more deep sea rescue vehicles capable at least of lessening the risk of cruising the depths, even if they could not have reached the greatest depths.

The prospect of gouging the sea bed for its wealth will always beckon the new prospector but the gut concern of man in working the sea has been and will be with food, not minerals. As his numbers on land increase, hunger, the oldest and strongest urge, will drive man to greater effort and more ingenuity to harvest the seas to feed the population which already crowds his planet.

It is not enough, as Professor Fye and his colleagues show us, to work with nature on its own terms in harvesting the sea. Man has it in his power to increase not only the yield from the sea but also its essential food values.

On February 2, 1967, the U.S. Food and Drug Administration gave a clean bill of health to what may be a new "wonderfood"—a fish protein concentrate, or *FPC*. This odorless, tasteless fish powder could make a significant contribution to lessening the pressure of a growing world population upon resources.

From the whole ocean, men today take only about 3 per cent of its potential animal resources. But the annual world-wide fish harvest, now about 55 million tons, is increasing at a rate of about 6 per cent, of which the U.S. share remains fairly constant at about 6 billion pounds.

Given appropriate international conservation measures the annual world harvest might even be quadrupled without depleting fish stocks. Moreover, a new science of farming the sea, or aquaculture, is coming into being which is already producing some astonishing results, particularly for shellfish of the higher commercial qualities.

But as we move toward a fuller harvest of the seas we must make strides not only in scientific research and development but also in statecraft and international law and understanding.

Fishermen should become herders, not hunters. We shall need new concepts and new legal protection to allow the development of methods of range management in the oceans, quite analogous to the methods used by cattle growers on land.

Even before that time, the problem of conservation in the oceans will be acute. For some species, particularly whales, it is already very serious. Present international fisheries commissions and other machinery for coping with the problem have proved erratic in performance, largely because of their inability to impose sanctions. As time goes on the depletion of species may occur at more rapid rates.

The hazards to sea life of ecological changes precipitated by unexpected, unwelcome by-products of commercial use are clearly on the increase. The Torrey Canyon incident illustrates the dangers of pollution arising from the sinking of even one of the new "supersize" tankers. Moreover, the greatest damage to wildlife was done in that case not by the spilled oil, but by the detergents used in an attempt to clean up the oil.

Dumping of sewage and other pollutants from land will undoubtedly affect at least the immediate coastal and estuary waters, especially with regard to their fertility, though pollution in the deep ocean may not be a serious problem for many years to come.

The effects on weather patterns of alterations to the water/air interface may also prove of growing importance. Steps taken to increase ocean productivity may have unexpected effects on rainfall over land.

A new sea-level canal across the Isthmus of Panama may have major effects on the biological life on both sides as a result of the mixing of the divergent life forms and the differing water temperatures.

These are but a few examples of the impact of industry and commerce on the sea environment.

The impulse to acquire and to profit can be expected to open new frontiers at sea as it has done on land. Investors will look for a fair deal. But the enlightened entrepreneurs, the scientists and the lawyers (see Chapters 1 and 2) are all concerned to see that wasteful competition is avoided, and that the patrimony of the seas is not despoiled or monopolized or withheld from the needy in the name of profit.

International Law of the Seas

The prospects of sea science and technology and the transfer of new hopes and national aspirations to the ocean realms are forcing the pace in evolution of the law of the sea.

Major legal, regulatory and policy issues are now posed with respect to provision for the settlement of disputes and for the ownership, control or regulation of ocean resources. There are differences of opinion with respect to the extent to which these could and should be resolved by giving more authority to international organizations.

There is no single law of the sea but a body of codes, international agreements, unilateral declarations, precedents, and traditional practices that affect activities on or under the surface of the high seas. Some of these have been rendered obsolete by new capabilities; most important, many major operations which are already possible, or soon will be, contain the seeds of dispute or may result in a misallocation of resources. Yet these activities are not now adequately covered by existing international law. As Professor Henkin points out in Chapter 2, there is need for more adequate law to govern such issues as: the reach of national sovereignty; ownership of the resources in the sea or under the seabed; liability for pollution; and conflicting uses of the sea.

The Geneva Conventions of 1958, which sought to establish guidelines on the exploitation of the continental shelf, are already under pressure as ambitions for wider exploitation mount, and as the developed nations, especially the coastal states, look to the sea to satisfy their wants.

As operations on the continental shelf and contiguous waters multiply, different geographic configurations and natural resources for different coastal nations will give rise to increasingly obvious anomalies, overlapping and unclear jurisdictions, and other sources of dispute.

The 1958 Geneva Convention essentially gave sovereign rights to the continental shelf to the coastal state out to a water depth of 200 meters, or to where the technology can reach (the so-called "exploitability clause"). As an equitable concept this essentially "open-ended" exploitability clause leaves much to be desired, for it gives those states bordering the oceans an opportunity to claim more and more of the seabed, further inhibiting other uses of the sea by other nations.

Professor Henkin in Chapter 2 has crystallized the essential differences of economic interest and potential among nations reflected in their opposing views about how wide the continental shelf should be.

The defenders of the wide shelf claim that a wide definition would encourage the coastal states to give up their stand for an "open-ended" definition, make for more liberality in the evolution of law defining exploitation of the deep seabed, and reassure coastal states by impeding the establishment of foreign mining installations which might mask more hostile activities.

Others urge a narrow shelf as more consistent with the growing ability and will of nations to exploit the deeper waters, and because a wider shelf applied around the world would involve curious, arbitrary and even preposterous imbalances of advantage. Most important, exclusive jurisdiction in the coastal state for mining tends to expand to exclusive sovereignty for other purposes, reducing the areas of freedom for others.

In the circumstances, Professor Henkin proposes that the legal concept of the continental shelf be redefined to eliminate the "exploitability" clause, and that the shelf, as redefined, be narrow, not wide, preferably not beyond the 200 meter depth.

But this issue is complicated by the fact that neither science nor commerce will stand still while the law evolves or nations bring themselves to negotiate. Already, in the "grey" zones or waters exploitation is going ahead. The prospecting, mining and petroleum interests are understandably concerned about the legal uncertainties surrounding activities at the "interface" of the continental shelf, as yet to be defined, and the deep seabed.

Professor Henkin suggests that there be a buffer zone *x* miles from shore which would be "deep" ocean in which mining could take place only by or with the consent of the coastal state but which would be subject to whatever regime is adopted for the seabed. A variation, which seems at least an approach to a solution, was put forward by the 33rd American Assembly on May 5, 1968. The suggestion was that the United States not claim and urge other nations not to claim permanent exclusive rights to resources beyond the 200 meter depth; the United States would issue licenses for exploitation in adjacent areas beyond that depth, subject to the condition that it will transfer to an appropriate international regime, which may be established for the deep seabed, licenses in areas subject to that regime, as ultimately defined and agreed.

As to the concept of territorial waters, the "expansive" school, comprised of nations which would have a limit of 12 miles or further, seems to be making headway. But a 12-mile limit all around the globe would reduce the "high seas" by some 3 million square miles. Familiar international channels like the Straits of Gibraltar subject to new uncertainty or contention.

There is already apparent a tendency of some nations toward a variable concept of territorial waters with special limits for special purposes, some reaching far out into what have been traditionally the "high seas."

Most American sea lawyers would probably agree that the territorial sea should be defined as narrowly as possible but would not rule out a 12-mile limit, provided that international freedom of passage through all international straits is assured.

Beyond territorial waters and the shelf, a great international debate is looming on the issue of the regime to govern exploitation of the resources of the ocean bed. As Professor Henkin observes, the deepest differences reflect different guiding principles.

Does the common good require that the resources of the ocean bed be opened up as soon as possible, even if this means expanding the advantages of the affluent and technocratic nations and allowing parts of the seabed to pass under their sovereignty? Or giving such nations preferential rights to those areas which they can exploit?

Or should the paramount principle be that the deep seas and their resources are the inalienable common heritage of all mankind? Can it not now be asserted that neither the bed of the deep sea nor its resources are subject to national appropriation?

Some would say yes, convinced that the world community should not tolerate a race among nations to seize the wealth of the deep ocean bed. They say it should now assert "preventive law to forestall race and grab," arrange for exploration and exploitation on behalf of the community, make the products fairly available and apply revenues to communal purposes.

This concept can be compared to that of Senator Claiborne Pell, whose Senate Resolution of November 17, 1967, calls on the United States Representatives at the United Nations to put to the General Assembly the basic principles "to govern the activities of nations in ocean space." Senator Pell's conception includes a conference in 1969 to define the outer boundaries of the continental shelf; an international agreement to insure that the deep seabed, its resources and subsoil beyond the Continental Shelf would not be subject to the sovereignty of any nation or group of nations; and proposals looking to the non-militarization of the ocean floor.

Many different legal patterns for exploitation of deep seabed mineral resources are possible, all with different implications for the long-term objectives of different nations. The United States and other major powers will evaluate any proposal for an international regime for the oceans in terms of their security and, in the absence of reliable arms control measures, are not likely to foreclose the seas to further development of weapons systems they consider defensive. Yet some kind of international agreement on ownership, regulation, and control will be necessary to extend arms control to the seas, to avoid conflict over resources, to allow the United States and other nations to operate in areas beyond their immediate coasts, to encourage private enterprise to contribute to the economic development of the Third World.

A laissez-faire approach could, in principle, be continued, but it is unlikely to be either acceptable or desirable. An untrammelled and therefore highly unstable competition among nations to seize the mineral wealth on the sea floor must be averted. The unseemliness of such a prospect is unlikely, however, to lead the maritime nations to embrace President Johnson's vision of an ocean floor preserved as a "legacy for all human beings." Nor will the developed nations be likely to accept, undiluted, a resolution of the Malta type introduced into the General Assembly by Ambassador Pardo of Malta, reserving the seabed to exclusive international jurisdiction. For the present the United Nations has established a committee of 35 nations to explore the issues and report back in 1968.

In principle, a nation can choose among four paths in the development of international authority over the oceans. It can follow a path of resistance to all but the barest minimum of international rules. That is the easy but selfish policy which most favors the advanced nations in the best position to exploit ocean resources. Or it can elect a second path leading through a series of bilateral agreements which might keep the complications of international organization to a minimum, but would also tend to favor the wealthier nations. A third path is toward vesting a measure of control in some kind of international organization. The fourth and perhaps most venturesome path would be toward actual ownership of land or resources by an international organization. The latter two choices, of course, favor the development of independent power in international organizations, and by implication some attrition or limitation of national power and freedom of action.

Thus, before a single alternative can be chosen, there are fundamental political issues to be resolved—issues involving the extension of existing patterns of nationalism and sovereignty to the oceans; the future development of international organizations—the United Nations or other mechanisms (e.g., Intelsat)—with some of the characteristics of government such as access to independent revenues and the ownership and control of substantial property; the allocation of revenues to internationally determined instead of nationally determined purposes; and the relationship of the military security of individual states to the determination of an acceptable international regime for the oceans.

Yet, the four choices are not mutually exclusive. Clearly a nation at any given time may be exploring all four paths simultaneously. How a nation decides and how it defines its long-term objectives with regard to the oceans may well shape in basic ways its whole attitude toward the development of the international community.

Whatever degree of authority nations may decide to vest in an international organization, the available international machinery does not appear to be adequate, either in its attributes or in its resources. Our contributors, including Professor Skolnikoff in Chapter 3, therefore contemplate the creation of an organism within the United Nations family with special responsibilities in respect of the exploitation of the non-living resources of the deep sea bed. As indicated by the 33rd American Assembly in May, 1968, its functions might include:

—issuance of licenses for agreed activities and international registration and regulation of such activities;
—collection of an agreed share of revenue for internationally agreed purposes, including benefits for developing nations;
—referral of disputes to international arbitration or adjudication;
—encouragement of research, exploitation and investment.

With respect to the living resources of the sea, stronger regulatory machinery is urgently needed to avoid the economic and physical waste of some current fishing practices.

National Organization

Professor Skolnikoff has also contributed his analysis of the kind of national organization for oceanology and ocean policy the United States will require to carry out both its national and international responsibilities. He queries whether present allocations for research and development are appropriate, whether arrangements for interchange between civil and military agencies and between government and the private sector are adequate and whether existing provisions for integrating ocean policy with U. S. foreign policy objectives are effective.

The analogy between the national space effort and the ocean effort is a facile but misleading one. Professor Skolnikoff dismisses the so-called "wet NASA" as a model inappropriate for the organization of our oceanological effort. Contrary to the pattern of our effort in space, we are not in the oceans pioneering in a vacuum by means of an almost exclusively governmental program. The American interest in the oceans is as old as the nation, it is shared by a variety of governmental and private bodies, and it includes extensive, long standing, and increasing private investment. It would simply be unrealistic and counter-productive to try to bundle maritime commerce, law, mining, fishing, defense, and foreign policy into one NASA-type package.

Although the parallel to NASA may not be valid, this does not mean that the problems of the seas are not urgent. Rather, as Senator Claiborne Pell has pointed out, in some ways the oceans may deserve higher priority because while we are not about to farm the moon, we can and must farm the seas.

It is also true, as Professor Skolnikoff remarks, that the very breadth of interest in the oceans hinders effective organization to meet its problems. The multiplicity of government agencies and the dispersion of its activities results in "scatteration."

Professor Skolnikoff applauds the important first step toward a marine policy represented by the establishment (under PL 89-954) of the interim National Council on Marine Resources and Engineering and the Presidential Commission which has been created to make recommendations for the future. He goes on to recommend that the future national effort be guided by two bodies, one a planning and coordinating group in the office of the President, and the other a new independent agency concerned with ocean engineering and resource development, the protection and improvement of the marine environment, and the promotion of new technologies and activities. Even so, it would be very doubtful if the new organizations should gather to themselves all the sea-related programs now spread through several agencies. They could promote a more effective "clustering" of operations and might serve to help correct an imbalance, which seems to worry some people, between the oceanographic activities and research sponsored by the Navy and all other efforts.

At the same time as the structure of the executive branch is revised to cope with oceanology, the organization of congressional committees ought to be considered. But just as there appeared little sentiment in 1968 for a "wet NASA" there did not seem to be much for a Joint Congressional Committee.

No aspect of national policy toward the oceans has greater importance than security. The vision of abundance from the sea, of maritime commerce as a peaceful link among nations, of international cooperation at sea ever growing and creating precedents for international organization, all depend in some degree upon maintaining the security of the seas, either through a traditional balance of forces or through arms control measures or both.

The balance of forces is a precarious one. If oil wells and mining operations can be established on the sea bed, so can strategic weapons systems. Despite certain advantages claimed for such installations in terms of distance from population centers, or the putative reinforcement of the network of reciprocal strategic deterrence which constrains the United States and the Soviet Union, the deployment of new systems might yet upset the equilibrium. It is to be hoped therefore that early agreement can be reached to prevent the deployment of weapons of mass destruction designed for use on the ocean floor.

Until arms control measures become effective, the condition of reciprocal deterrence looks at least like available insurance against general and disastrous war.

But the base on which the equilibrium rests is being troubled, not only by technological ferment, but also by shifts in the naval strategy and dispositions of the great naval powers.

The first three chapters of this book deal with the peaceful uses of the sea—with science and technology, with international law, and with national and international organization. The last three chapters explore change in its military uses, chiefly by three great powers.

The Changing Naval Roles of Britain, the Soviet Union, and the United States

The mission of the world's war fleets, the terms of their confrontation, and the composition of their forces are continuously modified by the world's increasing use of the sea, by competition to exploit the sea bed for military and civil purposes, and by developments in electronics, ship construction and weaponry. The undersea environment will be the locus of new forms of military effort. Bottom stations are possible essentially at any depth, and through excavations in the rock of the ocean bed, permanent living facilities or garrisons could be constructed. To an astonishing degree man is already capable of operating in vehicles or stations at great depth. The mines, shops, and culture of the depths, whether national or international, regulated or free, will impose new kinds of missions on naval forces. The prospects of seabed or shelf-based missile sites are real, and sea-stationed antiballistic missile systems far removed from population centers could be constructed.

Until a new international order emerges, and perhaps for sometime after, the rule of the seas will in the last analysis depend upon an international balance of power projected at sea by the world's warships, most of which are distributed among only two of the great maritime countries, the United States and the USSR. The accelerating decline at sea of a third—once mighty Britannia—must engage our attention. The stream of history is altering the balance of national power and the terms of naval strategy. While the Soviet Navy has moved into unaccustomed waters, the long British withdrawal from strategic positions east of Suez was speeded in 1968 by a balance of payments crisis aggravated by two maritime events: the closing of the Suez Canal and a strike of British dockworkers.

But the motives for British withdrawal as illuminated by our two Commonwealth authors, Professors L. N. Martin and Hedley Bull, do not all spring from economic or balance of payments difficulties. They include most importantly the antecedent liquidation of Empire. In times of stringency, especially, there is a certain difficulty in maintaining a fleet traditionally associated by the British subject and taxpayer with a world map, once colored imperial red but now confusedly particolored. A reaction against colonialism or neo-colonialism has something to do with it. So perhaps does the attraction of "going into Europe," but here it is unclear what is effect and what is cause, whether the new British conversion to Europe is the natural result of imperial renunciation or whether the entrance requirement for Europe is estrangement in the Commonwealth and from the Atlantic.

In any case an American cannot read of the comparatively meager world naval mission which the British would now assign themselves without some selfish national concern, especially since contractions in British air/sea power seem to occur annually and at greater than predicted rates. Nor can one consider, as Americans ought to do, the high quality of the British Navy, its recent services in the Indian Ocean, Red Sea, and Malaysian waters, and its general back-up of a British policy which has been America's principal foreign support without grave misgivings about the outcome of any new crisis in the old trouble spots. As strong as the British Navy still is, we should be aware as Professor Martin puts it, that "uncertainties must surround the future of a fleet the traditional justification of which has expired." If there is a "vacuum" east of Suez or in the Pacific, the United States can look for less and less help from diminished Great Britain in filling it.

One cannot suppress the fugitive thought that this long withdrawal might have been better managed by the English-speaking powers counselling together, that if the British motives were indeed economic, we Americans might have found some way to offset the costs at a time when our international accounts were healthier; and that even now it may not be too late to revive some form of the "special relationship" at sea, or even to explore some new form of association between the two most like-minded sovereign nations which could provide us both with more security and Britain with either an alternative to Europe or more leverage in negotiating its amalgamation in Europe.

In Chapter 4 Hedley Bull, the Australian military analyst, projects one very specific, meaningful, if limited contribution to this relationship. He points out that in the vast South Pacific area the United States has no bases closer to trouble than Pearl Harbor and Subic Bay. Even Simonstown in South Africa is, to say the least, uncertain. And he apparently takes at full value our promise to evacuate bases in Vietnam. Americans should carefully consider his proposal for American and Australian joint development of the base at Cockburn Sound in Australia.

The disposition of the free world navies is, of course, increasingly influenced by Soviet deployments and intentions. There can be no question but that the Soviet Union since the 50's has wished to play a more active role in the Third World, that its purposes have sometimes been thwarted by the greater logistic strength and adaptability of the free world (or by the obstruction of continental China); and that her developing capacity for limited warfare, and insurgency from the sea, plus the potential for conflict in its relations with China all constitute new and more volatile elements in the world military equation.

The Soviet Union may be reacting to or exploiting what it considers to be the decline of United States influence in Europe and elsewhere in the world. This can be heady stuff for pent-up Soviet power. Or, a credible interpretation of Soviet moves may be that they are in response to American operations or else in imitation of the stages of development of the senior U.S. and NATO navies. Thus, the addition by the Soviet Union of a small carrier or two and the expansion of its "naval infantry" need not in themselves signal aggressive intentions. But, as our Soviet affairs analyst, Professor Marshall Shulman points out in Chapter 5, in military affairs capabilities sometimes beget intentions.

The very newness of the situation in which the Soviet Union finds itself, the apparent crumbling of old barriers to its movement, the opportunities which beckon for using its navy to back diplomatic adventure all present danger of clashes through miscalculation or overreaching. The aftermath of the six-day Arab-Israeli war in 1965 saw Russian surface naval ships more active in the Mediterranean than in centuries.

Despite a widespread presumption that technology and geographic position and the conventional naval wisdom of the USSR ordained the submarine as its weapon of choice, the Soviet Union in 1968 showed renewed interest in a high sea surface force, augmented its amphibious elements, and was reported to be building a small carrier or carriers.

It is significant that this new dimension of Soviet power coincided with the development of new peaceful uses of the seas which may contain within them the seeds of new rivalries.

These are some of the considerations that lead Marshall Shulman to conclude that the alternatives of cooperation and conflict at sea are most starkly posed on the military side of ocean activities.

But the trend need not be to negative results. However we and the Soviet Union view each other's military stance, we have already proved that we can cooperate in research at sea, in the antarctic and in the sea of space and that we can reach other international understandings.

In Chapter 6 Mr. Gordon MacDonald seems to take a less relaxed view of thaw in the cold war and of the threat of recurring crises, particularly in the Third World and in the Southwest Pacific from which the British are retreating, at least that is the cumulative impression left with this reader by his somewhat chilling inventory of potential trouble spots in a capsule reconnaissance of the world.

Mr. MacDonald also sounds rather somber about the sparseness of overseas bases available to the United States and their insecurity. He points out usefully that the Soviet Union may now elect to conclude more overseas defense agreements with other countries, either as cause or effect of its enlarged naval capacities.

On the other hand he does not think the Communist Chinese are likely to develop a submarine-based nuclear force in the near future. He thinks rather that Peiping would choose to exert whatever pressures it may wish to bring to bear upon its neighbors through its land forces and presumably its capacity for subversion.

One is also left with the impression that despite the United States naval might which Mr. MacDonald catalogues, he perceives a lack of due emphasis and of Congressional support for the kind of U.S. naval force which could be most useful in the circumstances.

Insofar as Mr. MacDonald and our other contributors have speculated on the next decade, they do not foresee the doom of the navy as a result of technological advances nor any developments which would transform it out of recognition. While they perceive perhaps more than the usual lag in the application of new science to the naval art, the biggest changes in naval strategy by their account seem likely to rise from the political side of the political/military process, including fluctuations in relative national economic weights and productivity, changing concepts of national and imperial missions, and even alterations in popular psychology.

Most of the world's foreign commerce will still be carried in ships' bottoms, the protection of which will still be an air/naval mission even though the relevance of a naval strategy addressed primarily to protecting sea supply of Europe in a situation of all-out nuclear war is sharply questioned, particularly by Professor Martin. If such a catastrophe should occur, it is pointed out the enormous effort which has gone into building commerce-raiding and continental defense submarines on the one hand and an anti-submarine capability on the other could well prove useless.

While nuclear armaments remain in the stalemate of mutual deterrence (and our analysts seem to see the stand-off continuing, despite the implications of nuclear proliferation), a substantial and perhaps increasing proportion of the deterrent will be sea-borne or sea-stationed.

The submarine nuclear weapons system appears destined for long service. It seems unlikely that the means of maintaining surveillance on the oceans will ever approximate what is possible in the atmosphere; hence submerged military forces, and in particular deterrent forces, will continue to maintain an advantage which the science of defense shows scant promise of overcoming. Submarine warfare is likely to continue to favor the underwater force seeking to remain hidden, rather than the forces and instruments seeking to discover it.

A substantial undersea deterrent should continue to be valid at least through the decade of the 70's. This is true for any sizable new submarine force composed of true submersibles that exists or may be commissioned by countries not now in the lists.

The attractiveness of an undersea force for the Chinese is obvious and may prevail over contrary indications of costs, technological and industrial weakness, and the competing claims of a different kind of military effort designed against China's continental neighbors, including the Soviet Union.

Under the nuclear umbrella, the most probable form of armed international conflict is still seen to be limited in magnitude and area. And the importance of sea-power, sea-transport, and sea-generated intelligence in waging limited warfare and in keeping it limited receives an overdue appreciation from these analysts. One writer, Mr. MacDonald, does point out that in spite of its history of amphibious achievement, the United States Navy with its emphasis on the nuclear deterrent really needs a greater capability in the means of local warfare; helicopters, surface effect vehicles, fixed-wing aircraft, etc. At the same time it can be observed that a gun-shy United States Congress may refuse to support any such development, judging by Congressional reactions to the Pueblo and Liberty incidents in 1968 and its veto on the construction of fast deployment logistic support vessels, on the grounds that possession of such ships might make the U.S. involvement in limited wars more likely.

The problem of Vietnam in the spring of 1968 was treated gingerly by our contributors. One writer intimates that the acceptability of limited warfare as an option of national policy has been undermined by the struggle in Vietnam. But another, writing from Australia, sets up a brief balance sheet of debits and credits to the free world of limited warfare in South East Asia and in the Southwest Pacific which appears to come down on the positive side.

Paradoxically, the struggle in Vietnam, which might have been expected to focus politico/military thinking upon the future and upon developments in the wider area, such as the consequences of British withdrawal and our relations with the English-speaking powers, may instead have absorbed the planners' attention so completely as to scant some broader issues.

But if the Vietnam agony has moved toward a close as this writing appears, new currents of thought will be flowing in channels for peace, and the patterns of cooperation which the problems of the sea are enforcing upon mankind could be part of that network. Just as the sea contains and molds the whole earth, slowly but irresistibly shaping its contours, so may the coming together in the common ocean of so many problems mean that man will do better at solving them there than he has done on the selfish land, littered and cluttered by his past mistakes.

The sea way may be the new way to international understanding, cooperation and peace.

Paul M. Fye, Arthur E. Maxwell,
Kenneth O. Emery, and Bostwick H. Ketchum

1

Ocean Science and Marine Resources

In the field of oceanography the era of exploration and observation is drawing to a close, an exciting period of scientific investigation is in progress, and scientific knowledge is beginning to be applied to sophisticated engineering projects useful to mankind.

Not many years ago oceanographers assumed that the ocean environment changed so slowly that observations taken at one point in the ocean could be compared with similar observations at another point even though the observations were taken several years apart. Average conditions in the oceans could thus be established. With the availability of bigger and faster ships, improved instrumentation and data processing techniques, physical oceanographers are now concerned with dynamic fluctuations in the oceans both in space and in time. Present theories do not satisfactorily explain or predict all of the many fluctuations that have been observed over a wide span of time, but significant progress has been made in the development of theories which are permitting a basic understanding of the vast transport of water and energy throughout the total ocean system.

PAUL M. FYE *is president, and* ARTHUR E. MAXWELL, KENNETH O. EMERY, *and* BOSTWICK H. KETCHUM *are senior scientists at the Woods Hole Oceanographic Institution. Dr. Fye has taught chemistry, worked in research and development for the United States Navy, and since 1958 has served as director of Woods Hole; Dr. Maxwell has specialized in geophysical research both at Scripps Institution of Oceanography and as head of the geophysics branch, Office of Naval Research; Dr. Emery has taught marine geology for more than 20 years and is an authority on the world's continental shelves; and Dr. Ketchum has taught marine ecology and specialized in marine biology.*

In the studies of life within the sea, marine biologists are now well beyond the stage of simply classifying the abundant marine life found in the oceans. They have thus far identified over 200,000 species of plants and animals. Now they are asking questions about the extensive variations of fertility found in the sea, the interrelationships among various communities of animals living in the sea, and seeking an explanation to the distribution and evolution of these many different species.

The geologists and geophysicists have also made great progress in learning about the history of the earth by use of recently developed gravimeters, magnetometers, seismographs, and sampling techniques adapted to use within the oceans.

The full story of the rapid and exciting scientific developments in oceanography during the last decade are too complex and too extensive to be appropriate for this volume. We have concentrated on the resources—living, mineral and chemical—of the oceans rather than the physical characteristics or the complex phenomena that make this watery shell such an intriguing environment for investigation, exploration, and speculation.

A treatment of resources necessarily concentrates attention on the continental shelf where all the non-technical problems become more important and more difficult. National boundaries, ownership or lease rights on the bottom, and fishing rights are all more complex here than in the deep ocean. Nevertheless a proper consideration of marine resources should begin with a summary of the features characteristic of the deep ocean. The main physical, chemical and biological parameters can be identified in relatively simple terms.

The physiographic features consist mainly of:

—a continental shelf extending from the beach to a width as large as 800 miles with outer depths of 50 to 500 meters (here exist the principal mineral deposits and important fisheries activities which will be important in the immediate future).

—a continental slope slanting gently downwards from the shelf to the ocean depths of two or three miles at a slope generally less than 5°. The slope is scarred by great canyons somewhat similar in appearance to canyons on land.

—deep abyssal plains consisting of flatlands, many thousands of square miles in extent, beyond the slope.

—isolated mountain peaks dotting these plains at irregular intervals and occasionally rising high enough to become oceanic islands.

—mid-ocean ridges roughly bisecting the ocean basins and constituting the longest continuous mountain ranges in the world.

—a rift valley following the middle of the ridge almost its entire length.

The chemical features consist mainly of:

—a complex solution of dissolved chemicals ("salt") comprising the oceans' best known feature, with a concentration of about 35 parts per thousand.

—a surprisingly uniform chemical content of the approximately 40 chemicals constituting the common elements in the oceans' "salt."

—a vastly more dilute and less understood solution of trace elements, organic constituents (pharmaceuticals, proteins, fats, etc.) that support and permit life to exist within the sea.

The biological features consist mainly of:

—a variety (over 10,000 known species) of one-celled plants called phytoplankton that support all marine life through photosynthesis.

—an almost equally large variety of tiny animals called zooplankton that drift with the currents.

—an enormous variety (over 100,000 species identified) of invertebrates.

—fishes which range in size from a few centimeters in length to the large game fish weighing 1000 kilograms and more.

—mammals (whales, porpoises, seals, walrus) that form a curious classification which depends on the atmosphere for oxygen and includes some of the most intelligent animals in the whole sub-human kingdom.

This summary, though deceptively simple, provides some appreciation for the many aspects of oceanographic knowledge which have been necessarily omitted from this chapter.

Science of the Sea

Man's first desire to understand and use the sea undoubtedly dates back to his early development and his initial contacts with it. At that time, he could not realize the enormity of the sea or the complexity of the physical, chemical, biological and geological processes operating within it and at its boundaries. Nor could he begin to comprehend the vast potential the sea held in store in terms of energy, minerals and transportation. Although mankind has evolved a library of information concerning the ocean throughout historical time, it is only during the past decade that he has come to realize the true potentials of this seemingly unlimited resource, and to make significant efforts to take advantage of them. This belated realization can be attributed to the relatively recent development of an understanding of ocean phenomena and marine life sufficient to permit sophisticated technology to be applied meaningfully to the scientific exploration of the sea.

About three centuries before Christ, Aristotle delved into the biological wonders of the Mediterranean—making many significant observations of marine fauna and suggesting taxonomic classifications that have withstood the test of time. Nonetheless, more than two thousand additional years elapsed before the first concerted scientific effort was undertaken to explore the nature of the world ocean. The epic cruise of H. M. S. *Challenger* departed England in 1872 to collect depth soundings, water samples, and marine specimens. Some three and a half years and 70,000 miles later, after circumnavigating the globe, the ship returned with a collection of data and specimens which to this day are used as reference material. The voyage of the *Challenger* is generally acknowledged as the beginning of modern oceanography.

Oceanography as it is known today encompasses all of the scientific observations made on the fraction of the earth covered by sea water. Physics, mathematics, chemistry, biology and geology are used to study processes taking place within the ocean and at its boundaries; to study the life within the sea and the nature of the earth beneath it. Like geology, it is the study of a part of the real world and all of its interactions. Incomplete understanding of the ocean and its resources has been the chief deterrent against man's more complete utilization of the great resources of the sea. For example, the theoretical basis for determining ocean tides was developed as early as the seventeenth century by Sir Isaac Newton and refined by Lagrange in the eighteenth. And even though all major maritime nations have for many years had large organizations (U.S. Coast & Geodetic Survey, Liverpool Tidal Institute, Japan Meteorological Agency) studying them, we have been unable to formulate adequate theories to predict mid-ocean tides and to understand the role of internal and bottom friction in these motions. Our knowledge of the tides and our ability to predict them is still largely empirical.

HISTORICAL DEVELOPMENT

To project the future growth of our knowledge of the sea and hopefully to determine the extent to which this will have an impact on mankind's use of its resources, we must first review briefly how the science of oceanography has developed, its dependency upon technological advances, and the substantial increase that has taken place in cooperative research programs. Oceanography has progressed through three distinct periods; each of these is related to the efforts of great scientists and the tools that were available to them. It is not surprising that each of these periods concentrated on different scientific disciplines.

Age of ocean exploration—Early ventures upon the open sea by Phoenicians, Vikings and Columbus were made in search for unknown lands. To these intrepid adventurers, the oceans were but a means to reach new destinations. Much later, expeditions were organized solely to search out the unknown of the sea itself. The most significant of these was the cruise of the *Challenger* (1872–1876), which initiated the great age of ocean exploration that was to last for nearly three decades. This cruise is significant largely because of the scientific efforts of Sir John Murray, a geologist; and the chief scientist, Sir Wyville Thompson, a biologist and student of the naturalist Edward Forbes. Curiously, although Forbes might be called the founder of marine biology, he is best remembered for his erroneous prediction of an azoic zone in the ocean—a depth below which no life can exist. This has long since been disproved, but at that time his thesis provided the impetus for scientists to examine the great ocean depths for marine life. The dredge, a sounding rope and water sampling bottles were the main tools of this cruise. Fifty volumes have been produced on its scientific results, which included descriptions of thousands of new species of animals that had been collected as well as a rough charting of the major basins of the oceans.

Following the *Challenger,* Prince Albert I of Monaco used his fortune to undertake in 1885 a series of investigations of the Mediterranean and Atlantic Ocean. His vessel *Hirondelle* is nearly as legendary as the *Challenger*. Even though Prince Albert had a wide interest in scientific problems of the ocean, including bottom topography and ocean currents, his major interest centered on marine biology. In particular, he was intrigued by the giant squid. Prince Albert advanced the *Challenger* techniques only marginally by introducing baited traps and other devices to attract fish. The Musée Oceanographique, which he established at Monaco in 1910, contains many of these original pieces of equipment.

During this same period other wealthy individuals such as Louis and Alexander Agassiz and Anton Dohrn turned their attention to the sea. The Museum of Comparative Zoology at Harvard and the Stazione Zoologica at Naples remain as their legacies.

All of these early efforts were of an exploratory nature, intended to determine what lived in the sea, how the ocean moved and what depths it contained. The thread of commonality—if one existed—was the passionate interest of scholars in determining the type and distribution of life in the ocean. The Age of Ocean Exploration represented a major advance in marine biology.

Age of classical oceanography—While the age of classical oceanography somewhat overlapped the great era of exploration, the emphasis was markedly different. In the latter there was a concentration of effort by a group of Scandinavians on the development of theorems on ocean currents based upon the distribution of density of sea water.

Just before the turn of the century, Bjerknes first introduced these
ideas, which were expanded upon by his students, Sandström and Hel-
land-Hansen. In 1905, still another of Bjerknes' students, V. Ekman,
formulated his famous "Ekman Spiral" theory to explain the effect of
wind drag on ocean currents. Concurrently with these theoretical considerations, there was Fridtjof Nansen's development of a device to
collect a sample of sea water at any depth; and his refinements of the
reversing thermometer, which could obtain the precise temperature at
the same depth. With a knowledge of the temperature and a chemical
analysis of the water sample it became possible to calculate accurately
the water density. Many world-wide expeditions over a period of half a
century went to sea armed primarily with these simple instruments and
Bjerknes' elegant theories. Most famous was the cruise of the *Meteor*,
which occupied oceanographic stations over much of the Atlantic
during 1925–27. From these cruises there emerged the "giants" of
physical oceanography—Sverdrup, Defant, Schott and Wüst. Later the
theoretical work was refined by Munk and Stommel of the United
States and Stockmann of the Soviet Union. However, during this entire
period, the verification of theory relied principally upon measurements
made with Nansen bottles and reversing thermometers. Over five million of these measurements have been made at many depths and
geographical locations and these have yielded a description of the
general circulation of the ocean and a delineation of its principal
water masses. Even today, the Nansen bottle and reversing thermometer
are standard equipment aboard every deep-sea research ship.

It is noteworthy that a handful of men and two pieces of equipment
made such an impact on the science of oceanography.

Age of marine investigations—Immediately following the Second
World War there was almost an order of magnitude increase in oceanographic research compared with the pre-war period. This was stimulated by war-time projects related to the problems of detecting submarines. Sonars and magnetometers, developed to a high degree of
sophistication during the war, soon were found to be severely limited
by environmental conditions. Consequently, the governments of most
maritime nations embarked on liberal programs of support for oceanographic research which continued after the war. Although this support was directed at the study of both physical oceanography and the
ocean bottom, scientific interests, available technology and timeliness
directed the major effort toward sea floor studies.

Techniques developed during the war were quickly oriented toward
scientific use. Sonars evolved into precision echo sounders, and air-borne
magnetometers were converted for use aboard ship for the investigation
of the earth's magnetic field. The piston corer was developed, enabling

the collection of bottom samples up to 20 meters in length. Gravity meters, which heretofore required such stability for operation that measurements could only be made at sea aboard submerged submarines, were refined using different principles, thereby allowing measurements from surface ships. Seismic reflection and refraction techniques previously used on land were adapted for work at sea. The first measurements of heat flow through the ocean floor were made. Bottom photography at all depths became a well-developed art.

Because each of these measurements eventually became relatively simple to make at sea, it was not long before geophysical measurements of the sea floor approached a quality and quantity similar to those on land. Two decades of worldwide measurements of the structure of the sea floor have literally revised our concepts of how the earth has evolved. World-circling ridges have been discovered; major fractures have been found to exist under the ocean; and great trenches are known to encircle the Pacific. An examination of these major features along with gravity, earthquake, heat flow and magnetic data, give substantive evidence of sea floor spreading and continental drift. The significance of these results is only beginning to be realized.

A TIME OF TRANSITION

In a short treatise one cannot begin to do justice to the subtle factors molding the future of oceanography. We can infer, however, from this brief review a few salient conclusions: At one time oceanography was primarily the hobby of wealthy scholars who could afford the expense of satisfying their curiosity about the sea. These men were followed by a small but talented group who advanced oceanography importantly through the use of a few primitive instruments, a great deal of intellect and a modicum of ship time. More recently the keystone for success has been an advanced technology, which because of its high cost must rely heavily on support from governments. While all of these factors still play some role in today's oceanography, there can be no doubt that new technology will be of primary importance for some years to come.

In contrast with the past, all the various oceanographic disciplines now seem to be moving ahead together, although there appears to be a pervasion of pragmatism throughout. The application of results from ocean research seem to be about equally divided between problems having military significance and those with civilian potentialities. Submarine detection still remains the major problem to navies. Even though detecton ranges have increased many-fold, the problems of localization and identification and the ability to track enemy submarines continuously are not resolved. Unless the unexpected happens, the opaque water of the ocean will never become as transparent to sonar as the atmosphere is to radar. Hence it may be assumed that governments will continue to support vigorous programs in ocean-ography because of the strategic value of the ocean as well as its economic potential.

Fortunately the U.S. Navy has not restricted its program of ocean research and engineering only to military applications. With an un-usual farsightedness, it has supported research on a broad basis, estab-lishing the foundation of knowledge of the sea upon which present programs of exploitation are based. Similarly the Navy's engineering programs have provided the tools for modern research, have developed an accurate and world-wide navigation system and have supported the bulk of engineering research on materials and power sources essential for the evolution of deep submersibles. Results from the man-in-the-sea program, for example, are now used by the offshore oil industry. Therefore, governmental support, whether intended primarily for mili-tary purposes or not, will have an important impact upon the future exploitation of the vast ocean resources.

THE NEW TECHNOLOGY

Ships—An essential element in oceanography is an ability to occupy the sea for the purpose of making observations. Many platforms have been used—the foremost being the research ship. Since the War, the research fleet has consisted mainly of converted naval or commercial vessels of World War II or earlier vintage, with notable exceptions such as the Woods Hole Oceanographic Institution's *Atlantis,* built in 1930 expressly for oceanographic research. Recently, there has been a world trend to replace and expand this obsolescent fleet primarily through the construction of ships designed for research from the keel up, utiliz-ing the latest technology available. Major shipbuilding activity has taken place in the United States, Russia, Canada, Japan, Germany and Great Britain. An illustration of the magnitude of this activity can be shown by examining the situation in the United States. Since 1959, forty new research ships have either been built or funding for their construction has been authorized by Congress. Additionally, 24 ships have been converted for research work. This represents a significant portion of the total U.S. oceanographic fleet, which numbers about 80 ships. Cost of the new ships ranges from 5 to 20 million dollars, depend-ing upon the size. A preference for medium-sized ships (around 2,000 tons or 200 feet in length) exists among American oceanographers. This is in contrast to the 4,000–6,000 ton research ships preferred by the Soviet Union, Germany and Great Britain. For most purposes, the medium-sized ships appear to be more efficient. However, for some work, especially in high latitudes, the additional size is desirable.

More important than size is the innovation of new ideas in ship construction. Ship design has been notoriously conservative, and experimental ships have been the exception. The recent introduction of cycloidal propellers on research ships to provide greatly increased maneuverability is considered by many to be extreme. To some extent it is also considered extreme to construct a large sea-going catamaran capable of handling heavy objects between its hulls. As yet, hydrofoils and air-cushion craft have not been considered for research use despite their ability to transit between observational stations at relatively high speed. The future is likely to see a trend toward more specialized ships. An abortive attempt along these lines was made with the Mohole Drilling Ship. Two deep draft submarine hulls, arranged catamaran style, were to support and stabilize a drilling platform nearly an acre in size and sixty feet above the water. Unfortunately Congress cut off funds for the project before the ship was completed. In spite of this, the engineering has survived and the offshore drilling companies are now utilizing the design. Meanwhile, the government has retrenched to a more conservative program which uses a standard ship hull for deep sea drilling exploration.

Buoys—The continuous monitoring of the oceans is too big a job for research ships alone. Consequently, a system of placing instruments in the ocean which can record the changes in such features as water movement, temperature, salinity, density, etc., on a continuous basis, has required the development of deep moorings supported by buoys at or near the ocean surface. Just as the Nansen bottle and reversing thermomometer played a major role in the determination of the general circulation of the ocean, the deep-moored buoy with its automatic measuring and recording equipment is the tool the modern physical oceanographer is relying upon to understand the variability of ocean circulation. The first successful deep-moored buoys were employed in 1950 to measure wave heights in the A-bomb tests at Bikini. At that time the wave sensing equipment had to be located at or near the sea surface and fine steel piano wire used for mooring. Life expectancy for these buoys was only a few months. Buoy systems now have sensing elements located at many depths extending to the bottom, which may record their signals either internally or transmit them to the surface float for recording or for further telemetering to shore or shipboard receiving stations. Synthetic lines have replaced piano wire, and elaborate releasing mechanisms are used to retrieve sub-surface systems. It is not uncommon for buoys to be set for periods greater than a year. The amount of data collected by these systems is so great that they must be handled and analyzed by very large computers. Buoys have grown in size from six feet diameter to over 40 feet. These larger buoys—completely self-contained with power supply, computers, tape recorders, radio receivers and transmitters—are designed for one year's unattended service. A single moored station of this complexity may cost as much as a quarter or half million dollars, depending upon the sophistication and number of sensing elements.

In 1968 oceanographers and meteorologists were considering the establishment of networks of buoys, which would contain an array of many smaller buoys clustered around one of these larger types. Thousands of buoys were thought to be necessary for a network sufficiently dense to meet the requirements of weather and ocean environmental predictions on a world-wide scale. The capital investment in a large-scale moored buoy program to monitor a single ocean basin can easily exceed a hundred million dollars, with operating expenses on a similar scale.

Another class of buoys widely used by oceanographers is the free-floating or drifting buoy. These can be either surface or sub-surface types. In general, the sub-surface types are neutrally buoyant designed to float at an intermediate depth. They contain sonic devices permitting the buoys to be tracked thus identifying current trajectories. Recent models used for tracing large scale ocean currents have been tracked at distances as great as 800 miles. Some of the free-floating surface buoys have attained the size of small ships and actually have been manned for periods of a few months. A notable example is the *Flip* (350 feet long and 20 feet diameter) of the Scripps Institution of Oceanography. *Flip* is towed to location in a horizontal position; then one end is flooded and the buoy assumes a vertical orientation. When this large buoy is maintained in a vertical attitude it becomes extremely stable, permitting special work to be carried out.

Because buoys allow certain observations to be taken at a cost small compared with a ship doing the same operation, it can be anticipated that their use will be greatly expanded. However, it is easy to foresee many legal questions arising in connection with the loss and liability of some of these buoys.

Submersibles—The first free-diving, deep submersible was built in 1948 under the direction of balloonist Auguste Piccard. He simply adapted the same principle to go down in the sea as he had used to go up in the air. For financial reasons, eventually his submersible, FNRS-3, became the property of the French Navy and was operated with Auguste Piccard as consultant. Nearly a decade later his son Jacques designed and constructed a similar craft, the bathyscaph *Trieste,* which was used by American scientists in 1957 for a series of acoustic experiments in the Mediterranean. Ironically, the following year the U.S. Navy purchased *Trieste* along with the services of Jacques Piccard.

This marriage of convenience led to a dive on January 23, 1960, to the ocean's greatest depth, the Challenger Deep at 35,800 feet. During this early period of development only minor scientific results were accomplished, but the experience proved beyond a doubt that the ocean depths were forever after technically accessible to man.

The *Trieste* was a cumbersome vehicle weighing 32 tons and requiring 60 tons of gasoline for buoyancy. Its principal mode of operation was in a vertical direction with limited horizontal maneuverability. A second research submersible, *Alvin,* was launched in 1964 at the Woods Hole Oceanographic Institution. Structurally, it differed from the *Trieste* by depending principally upon the volume of the pressure-tight personnel sphere for buoyancy. Using the best steel available, this allowed for a safe operating depth of 6,000 feet. *Alvin,* with a displacement of 14 tons, is highly maneuverable with a top speed of two knots and a submerged endurance of 13 miles at $1\frac{2}{3}$ knots.

Both of these vehicles were acquired with basic research as the motivation. However, it took two tragic marine disasters to bring home the full realization of the capabilities and needs for these types of submersibles. The first was the loss of the submarine *Thresher* in 1963, in 8,400 feet of water with no survivors. The *Trieste,* being the only vehicle available to go to that depth, participated in the search for the submarine's debris. The second disaster was the collision of two Air Force planes in 1966 over Palomares, Spain, in which a thermonuclear weapon was lost in the ocean. On this occasion, *Alvin* located the bomb in 2,800 feet of water after two months of search involving 34 dives. More than anything else, these two events stimulated an accelerated construction program of deep submersibles.

About the same time as *Alvin* was built, another research submarine, the *Aluminaut,* was being constructed in the United States. As the name implies, the hull was fabricated from aluminum. The designed operating depth was 15,000 feet, but manufacturing defects prevented the achievement of this depth. *Aluminaut* has a capacity to carry six persons, compared with a maximum of three for previous submersibles. Its endurance is 100 miles at a speed of three knots. Following these pioneering vehicles, over two dozen research submersibles have been built in the United States which have depth capabilities from a few hundred to about eight thousand feet. A parallel development of submersibles has taken place in France under the direction of Jacques Cousteau and the French Navy. To a lesser degree, the Japanese have been active in the design and construction of deep research submersibles.

During these few years of operation the scientists have become appreciative of and dependent upon these craft. They allow geologists to

sample precise outcrops, to examine visually structures of the bottom
and to follow salient features for several miles. Biologists have discovered an abundance and variety of life on the bottom that were heretofore thought inconceivable. It has been possible to identify the mid-
water plankton causing the scattering of sound as recorded on echo
sounders and sonars. Oceanographers are now designing experiments
using instruments that require a submersible to place and recover them
from the ocean bottom. These vehicles have become an integral part
of the oceanographer's technology.

Capital investment in small submersibles varies from a few hundred
thousand dollars to a few million, depending, of course, on the size,
endurance and depth range. Small, versatile research craft with 1,000
feet depth capability cost around a half million dollars, while the more
elaborate submarines that are to be used for rescue and salvage may
reach ten times this cost. Newer technology utilizing titanium or glass
pressure hulls promises to reduce the cost per foot of depth markedly.
It is not inconceivable that miniature glass submersibles will soon
become as common for recreational purposes as the aqualung. At the
other extreme in cost is the small nuclear powered research submarine
developed by the U.S. Navy. The first vehicle, designated NR-1, will
be able to carry seven persons for extended periods at continental
shelf depths. Its development cost will probably exceed a hundred
million dollars.

In addition to manned submersibles, there are several families of
unmanned vehicles. These range from towed platforms to remotely
controlled torpedo-like craft. As the reliability of these has increased,
they have become more popular because of the lesser expenses and
hazards involved.

Bottom and sub-bottom stations—A natural extension of undersea
vehicle construction is the establishment of fixed stations on or in the
sea floor. Already preliminary experiments have been carried out in
water depths up to 600 feet. The technology is available to extend this
to any ocean depth; only the motivation and money are lacking. It is
likely this will be done first on an experimental basis for research purposes. Any large scale effort will probably be deferred until there are
national requirements of a military or prestige nature.

Much of the life support technology developed for space programs
can be directly applied in compact bottom capsules. Unless the station
size warrants use of a nuclear reactor, a major problem is the power
requirements for extended periods.

Consideration also has been given to excavation in the consolidated
rocks beneath the sea floor. There appear to be no technical reasons

why large bases, similar to deep mines, could not be constructed under the ocean floor with access by locks on the sea bottom.

Aircraft and satellites—Man's romantic inclination toward ships undoubtedly helps explain his lack of aggressiveness in the use of aircraft for oceanographic research. An oceanographer naturally is a sailor. But it has been the space program in its quest for useful applications of earth satellites that has focused attention on the benefits to oceanography which flow from overhead observations of the ocean surface. Radiation measurements and the photography of large surface areas have provided useful information on ocean circulation. Other observations are being considered; however, the satellite's chief handicap is its remote distance from the ocean and its access only to the ocean's surface. This apparent disadvantage is also proving to be an asset in terms of navigation and communication. The existing satellite navigation system allows a ship to determine its position with an accuracy of better than a tenth of a mile, thus satisfying one of oceanography's greatest needs. Similarly, satellite communication is likely to be the key technological link permitting a global ocean buoy network.

Stimulated particularly by satellite activities, the aircraft now plays a more prominent role in oceanography. The ability to have precise navigation aboard both aircraft and ship enables the two vehicles to work in concert. Observations taken by one platform may be correlated with those taken from the other. Obviously, parameters such as the earth's magnetic field and the sea surface temperature can be measured much more rapidly with an aircraft. Through the use of drop-sondes and techniques to deploy and retrieve instruments in the ocean solely by aircraft a new phase is opening. In this type of operation the aircraft is no longer restricted to surface observations, and data may be obtained from any depth, including samples from the sea bottom.

Technological developments—Many broad technological areas must be developed further to meet some of the demanding requirements of the ocean environment. New materials must be developed. In order to achieve great depth in submersibles, a high strength to weight ratio is necessary. The present state of the art in the field of metallurgy does not permit sufficient payload at great depths to meet weight requirements for propulsion and equipment. High strength steels have been the most common material used for pressure capsules; however, welding problems with the thick plates and corrosion at the high pressures in sea water present difficulties. Titanium alloys have looked attractive because of their superior strength to weight ratio and their resistance to corrosion. Aluminum is another light weight metal used extensively in oceanographic equipment. Glass and glass-reinforced plastics appear to hold very high potential for deep sea work. They are both strong and corrosive resistant. Brittleness and difficulty to fabricate still present problems for these materials.

Power supply is another area requiring additional development. Remote and long-term operations make conventional systems unattractive. Fuel to energy conversion must be accomplished with a high degree of efficiency. Dependent upon the power requirements and endurance, the primary candidates for extensive use in ocean installations are: batteries, fuel cells and nuclear sources. None of these systems are developed to the degree of efficiency that existing demands require.

Even relatively simple equipment such as remote sensing devices that are used to measure various ocean parameters become complicated and difficult to maintain over long periods in the ocean environment. Corrosion and biological fouling plague nearly every known sensor, and it is difficult to have an instrument maintain calibration if left unattended for extended periods. Interactions among the many physical, chemical and biological properties of the sea often make the measurement of various parameters difficult.

Ocean engineering—A large fraction of the engineering development related to the oceans has taken place within the United States. Cousteau, at Monaco, has contributed significantly with many new concepts and he has pioneered undersea work both with divers and submersible vehicles. Countries such as Germany and Great Britain appear to have made relatively small engineering contributions compared with their interests in the sea. Although the Soviet Union has led the world in both tonnage and number of new ships built for ocean research, the available evidence indicates only minor Soviet engineering innovations.

Within the United States several new ocean engineering facilities have been established to attack the specialized problems encountered in the sea. These are located within the government, industry and academic communities. Most extensive are the Navy laboratories, which have reoriented their interests to ocean engineering problems. Their activities include: deep submersibles, man-in-the-sea, materials, instrument design, high pressure problems, and ship design. Industry has been particularly aggressive in the areas of deep submergence and man-in-the-sea, having invested sizable amounts of their own capital. Some of the large aero-space companies have undertaken ocean-related programs in anticipation of a shift of government funding to subsidize and stimulate the exploitation of the ocean resources. In the academic community, curricula in ocean engineering have been established in more than a dozen universities. These were non-existent less than five years ago. University "Departments of Ocean Engineering" are now common, and federal support through the newly established Sea Grant

Program most certainly will encourage their rapid growth. All indications are that within the United States ocean engineering is progressing
through the same stages as aeronautical engineering did several decades
ago.

Marine Resources

One who wishes to investigate the resources of the ocean must
consider three separate but related questions: (1) What and where are
the resources? (2) What is their value? (3) To whom do they belong?
Answers to these questions involve science, economics, and law. We
wish to consider briefly all three questions before proceeding in greater
detail with the first one.

In a broad way, the resources of the ocean can be grouped into three
main categories: chemical—materials that are dissolved in the water,
biological—plants and animals that live in the water, and geological—
minerals that occur on or beneath the bottom. As shown by Table 1,
the production of these resources from the ocean amounted to $10.5
billion in 1964, a large amount but still small in contrast with an estimated $333 billion production from the land areas of the world. If
evenly distributed, the total production from land areas of the world
(Table 1) averaged $2200 per square kilometer per year; for the United

TABLE 1. *Important Productivity Statistics**

	United States		Entire World	
	Ocean	Land	Ocean	Land
Resource ($10⁹)				
Chemical	0.1	0.1	0.3	0.2
Biological	0.4	45.0	6.4	260.0
Geological	0.9	20.0	3.8	73.0
Total	1.4	65.1	10.5	333.2
Area (10^6 km²)	—	9.4	361.1	148.9
Continental Shelf	3.4	—	26.4	—
Population (10^9)	—	0.19	—	3.22

* Dollar values are in terms of returns to the producers: fishermen, farmers,
miners. Refining or preparation, transportation, and retailing may constitute the
major costs to consumers. All data are for 1964, and were compiled from numerous
governmental and industrial publications.

States alone the average was $6900/km²/year.

The resources are not evenly distributed, nor are they evenly de-

veloped either on land or in the ocean. Comparison of the areas of
ocean and of land with the production from each shows that the ocean
as a whole is a small supplier ($29/km²/year). However, the most im-
portant part of the ocean is the continental shelf from the viewpoint of
resource value, not necessarily transportation or military values. All of
the chemical resources, all of the geological resources, and about 90
per cent of the biological resources have come from the shelf. Thus the
world's continental shelves with their area of 26.4 million km² supplied
$9.9 billion worth of resources during 1964, an average of $370/km²/
year. For the United States alone this average is nearly the same,
$400/km²/year. These shelf productivities are only 5 to 17 per cent of
the land productivities, but probable future technological developments indicate that great increases in the productivity of the shelf can
be expected, particularly in chemical and geological resources. Because
of this potential increase in productivity and because of increasing
demands for the resources, the shelf areas are the sites of increasing
claims and counterclaims for ownership, including the rights to tax as
well as to exploit. Claims are pressed hardest for geological resources
(which do not move about because they are part of the sea floor).
Claims are almost as great for biological resources (most of which have
limited movement), because on a world basis the annual production is
greater than geological and chemical resources combined, and because
world population pressure has led to increasing demands for food.
Claims are least pressed for rights over chemical resources (which are
dissolved in the water and are free to move with the water), except
where pollution by wastes from land (a reverse sort of chemical resource) is becoming increasingly important.

From the viewpoint of population, Table 1 permits calculations that
show the worldwide average production of natural resources is $103/
person/year from the land and $3.06/person/year from the continen-
tal shelf. For the United States alone corresponding figures are $343
and $7.16.

Geological Resources

Many proponents of sea-floor mining have compiled long lists of
minerals that have been recovered from the sea floor mostly by general
scientific expeditions. They listed these minerals in the interest of com-
pleteness of compilation, but only a few of the minerals have any
possibility of being economically mined, and fewer still actually have
been mined from the sea floor. Probably all of the minerals for which
sea-floor mining is significant (production of more than $1 million
during 1964) are listed in Table 2. A few other minerals are included

TABLE 2. *Value of Production of Geological Resources from the Ocean and the Land* (10^6)*

	United States		Entire World	
	Ocean	Land	Ocean	Land
Authigenic				
Phosphorite	0	160	0	375
Manganese	0	3	0	423
Detrital				
Sand and Gravel	35	860	100	2000?
Titanium	9?	11?	33	37
Zircon	1?	0	11	0
Tin	0	0	5	460
Diamonds	0	0	4	284
Monazite	0?	0?	1.5	0.3
Iron	0	800	0.7	5300
Gold	0	50	0	1310
Organic				
Oil and Gas	800	10,500	3600	27,500
Sulfur	15	100	15	240

* Dollar value is at import rate. All data are for 1964 and were compiled from numerous governmental and industrial publications.

in the table because so much has been written about them that they are associated with sea-floor mining in the minds of many laymen.

The list of minerals in Table 2 is subdivided into three main groups: authigenic, detrital, and organic. Authigenic minerals are precipitated from solution in sea water; the process is so slow that recognizable deposits occur only where other kinds of sediments are excluded. They are mostly restricted to thin surface layers. Detrital minerals are ones that were weathered and eroded from strata on land, transported to the ocean mostly by streams or sea-cliff erosion, and deposited as widespread layers on the sea floor. Useful deposits are much thicker than those of authigenic minerals, ranging from one to more than 100 meters. Organic minerals result from activities of living organisms; because they are easily destroyed, these minerals occur only at depths of hundreds or thousands of meters beneath the sea floor.

Within each group the minerals are arranged in order of decreasing value of annual production from the sea floor of the entire world. The total value of sea floor production of these minerals during 1964 was $3.8 billion. The value of the same minerals mined on land was $38 billion, only a bit more than half their $73 billion total production of all minerals on land.

AUTHIGENIC MINERALS

The two chief minerals that are formed by chemical precipitation from sea water are phosphorite and manganese nodules. Both are known only as thin surface deposits.

Phosphorite—Phosphorite occurs mostly in depths shallower than 300 meters. It ranges in grain size from less than one millimeter to more than one meter, and is a brown hard mineral that encloses sand, gravel, calcareous organic remains, and pieces of earlier phosphorite. Within the nodules are wavy interfaces that represent former depositional surfaces which were exposed so long that they became covered with thin films of manganese oxide and grains of another authigenic mineral, glauconite. Fossils in some of the enclosed early nodules are Miocene in age; their presence indicates that older strata had been eroded so that residual concentrations of nodules remained to serve as nuclei for much later deposition of new phosphorite. The mineral is a complex tri-calcium fluorcarbonate phosphate, containing less than 30 per cent P_2O_5 for sea-floor nodules, and commonly more than 31 per cent P_2O_5 for land ones that have been enriched through natural leaching by ground water.

The sea-floor deposits of phosphorite occur only in areas where floods of detrital and other sediments are excluded, usually by isolation atop shallow banks or at the seaward edge of continental shelves where sediments from shore are diverted by submarine canyons. The best known large deposits are off southern California and northwestern Mexico, off Peru-Chile, off the southeastern United States (Fig. 1), and off the Union of South Africa. Probably large deposits also occur off northwestern Africa and western Australia, but little field investigation has taken place in these places. With the exception of the deposits off southeastern United States, all of these areas are characterized by intense upwelling of phosphate-rich ocean water; they also lie off mid-latitude deserts that supply little detrital sediment.

Each of the two phosphorite deposits off the United States have been estimated to contain between one and two billion tons. Each has the same general tonnage as the Florida landpebble phosphate deposit that has supplied about 70 per cent of U.S. requirements and 30 per cent of world production. Even larger deposits occur in Idaho, Montana, and Wyoming; smaller ones are in Tennessee. In fact, the reserves on land in the United States amount to at least ten billion tons. The total United States production during 1964 was 23 million tons, with an average value of $7 per ton. More than 90 per cent is used as fertilizer and the rest in the chemical industry. The several hundred years' supply on land, the low unit price, the lesser P_2O_5 content of sea-floor

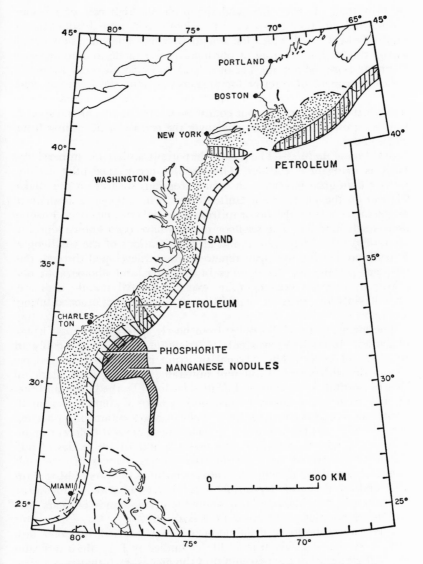

FIGURE 1. *Most Favorable Areas for Some Potential Geologic Resources off the East Coast of the United States.*

deposits than of land ones, and the probable high cost of offshore mining indicate that phosphorite is unlikely to be mined from the sea floor off the United States for several decades. The only substantial attempt at offshore mining of phosphorite was made in 1961 when a company leased about 125 km of a bank top off California from the U.S. Department of Interior for $122,000; in 1965 the lease payment was returned to the company by the United States. Perhaps mining will occur first near phosphate-poor countries, where the cost of transportation from other source areas may cover the extra cost of mining from the sea floor.

Manganese nodules—The second important authigenic mineral deposit is manganese nodules. The nodules occur at depths usually greater than 4000 meters, with some exceptions such as on the Blake Plateau off the southeastern United States, where they are as shallow as 300 meters. They also occur in fresh-water lakes of northern Europe and North America. The sea-floor nodules have been known since at least 1875, when they were found at many stations of the Challenger Expedition. During the 1950s renewed interest developed through the frequent presence of the nodules in dredgings and photographs obtained by deep-sea oceanographic expeditions. All nodule sites are ones having low rates of deposition of detrital and other diluting sediments.

The manganese nodules range from nearly spherical through irregular shapes to massive pavements of indefinite extent but probably at least tens of meters. The internal structure is irregularly layered or concentric, with layers of different mineralogy ranging from black to brown. Detrital and organic sediment is enclosed by the layers, and the center nucleus is commonly a shark tooth, a piece of pumice, or a small stone. Many nodules on the Blake Plateau also contain phosphorite, part of which has been replaced by manganese. Several different manganese minerals are present in the nodules, and all are oxides of the metal. Their layered arrangement results from changes in rate and nature of deposition during the probably millions of years of history of each nodule. Rates of deposition based upon radioisotope measurements range from thousands to hundreds of thousands of years per millimeter, with long intervals of no deposition.

Chemical composition of the nodules is highly varied, but some important elements are given in Table 3. Studies by J. L. Mero indicate regional variation in the percentage of the metals, such that maximum percentages may be as much as two or three times the averages given in the table. Tonnages on the sea floor are probably in the order of 10^{11} to 10^{12}; in fact, even the rate at which the manganese is accreting

TABLE 3. *Some Chemical Components of Manganese Nodules (per cent of dry weight)*

	Pacific Ocean	Blake Plateau
Manganese	24.0	16.0
Iron	14.0	17.0
Silicon	9.0	11.0
Nickel	1.0	0.4
Copper	0.5	0.2
Cobalt	0.4	0.3
Ignition Loss	26.0	24.0

may be several times the rate at which it is being mined by man from land sources, about 6 million tons per year.

Present reserves on land of the most abundant metal, manganese, are adequate for several hundred years at their present rate of use mainly as a toughener for steel. However, the United States produces only about 2 per cent of its needs, and during 1964 it imported 1.4 million tons of manganese at $54 per ton mainly from Brazil and Gabon. Other production and imports were for lower-grade manganiferous ores. Mining of the manganese nodules on the sea floor has been proposed, and a few large-scale tests have been made. However, severe metallurgical problems are caused by the abundance of silicon in the nodules. The thought also has been expressed that the nodules might be mined mainly for their contents of copper, nickel, and cobalt. Closer examination shows that the ratios of these metals are out of balance with present consumption, such that if copper equal to U.S. imports were obtained, the accompanying nickel and cobalt would flood the market, lower the price, and probably reduce the economic return below the costs of mining. In any event, the Blake Plateau nodules that are shallowest and nearest the mainland United States are by far the poorest in mineral value known on the entire sea floor, and there seems to be no simple cheap mechanical or chemical method of upgrading them. One other important problem of mining is that a huge capital investment is needed. This requires a very large daily recovery to offset interest and other costs; thus production could well depress world prices enough that the operation would become uneconomical. As a result, neither the Blake Plateau nodules nor the better but more distant ones of the deep Pacific Ocean are likely to be mined commercially for at least several decades. If the United States government were to heavily subsidize the mining and milling of nodules to encourage a supply of manganese independent of imports, the date of production would be advanced.

DETRITAL MINERALS

The term "detrital minerals" is a broad one, encompassing all minerals derived from the weathering and erosion of rocks, mainly on land. These rocks, including all igneous, metamorphic, and sedimentary types, consist chiefly of the light minerals quartz and feldspar with small percentages of many other minerals. Most of these other minerals have little value, but some of the rarer ones that contain little silicon are exceedingly valuable. Most of these latter minerals have high specific gravities, 4 to 21 times denser than water. During transportation by streams, currents, and waves their high density allows them to become separated from the lighter (2.6 specific gravity) quartz and feldspar.

Sand and gravel—The quartz and feldspar, along with rock fragments and shell debris, is ordinary sand and gravel. Although shells are organic in origin, they occur with the detrital minerals in a continuous sequence from 0 to 100 per cent. Because of this graduation, the fact that broken shells are moved and deposited by currents as though they were detrital in origin, and because most uses are similar, no distinction is made here between sand and gravel or shells.

Uses of the material are mainly for beach replenishment, land fill, and concrete aggregate. As shown by Table 2, nearly $900 million worth of sand and gravel were mined and used in the United States during 1964, at sand pit prices of about $1 per ton. About $35 million worth of sand, gravel, and shells were dredged from the sea floor during 1964 mainly to deepen navigational channels, create small-boat harbors, and to provide construction material in areas such as New York City and low coastal areas bordering the Gulf of Mexico where cheaper sources are not available. Added costs of offshore dredging yielded a unit value of $2 to $3 per ton. Similarly, the need for sand and gravel off England and elsewhere in Europe resulted in the development of sea-floor supplies. An area of shells off Iceland also has served as the source of raw material for a Portland cement factory. In Israel and Lebanon the need for sand to be used largely in concrete blocks has temporarily been satisfied by mining of beaches in the absence of cheap offshore dredging. The beaches have been so depleted that a large storm during 1967 was able to remove much of the remaining sand and expose previously unknown Phoenician and Roman seawalls. Offshore sources are to be dredged in order to replace the beaches. Need for augmenting beaches in the United States has resulted indirectly from such engineering errors as overprotection of beaches by groins, building of many small harbors protected by breakwaters, isolation of sources of sand by dams across streams and seawalls in front of sea cliffs, and construction of hotels and other buildings far out on once-wide beaches.

Sand and gravel are probably the cheapest of all materials recovered by offshore dredging. The material is low-cost because it is abundant, shallow, thick, and able to be transported cheaply and directly by dredge or pipeline. The main problem to be faced is that the site of removal should not be so close to shore that losses from beaches result from subsea movement of sand toward the dredged area. Studies of the sediments that cover most continental shelves of the world show that most of the seaward two-thirds of the shelves are floored with sand that is coarser than sand nearer shore, and that it is iron stained in response to long exposure on the bottom. Where studies have been reasonably thorough samples and photographs show the presence of empty shells of oyster and other shellfish that in life are restricted to depths of only two or three meters. These shells have been found at depths as great as 130 meters, and they are associated with fresh-water peat, elephant teeth, and other evidence that show the continental shelf was formerly exposed as dry land.

Radiocarbon dates on shells and peat in the relict sediment exhibit increasing age with increasing depth. Ages as great as 15,000 years occur at the shelf edge; this means that the sand is a relict deposit formed when sea level was lowered by the growth of glaciers which trapped water in the form of snow and ice. When the glaciers partly melted, some of the water completed its cycle from the ocean back to the ocean and then sea level rose to its present intermediate position. When sea level was lowest, about 150 meters below the present level, streams eroded wide valleys across the then land areas; these are now occupied by large estuaries that trap most of the river-borne sediment. Until the estuaries have become filled, little sediment can escape from them to bury the relict sediment. An estimated 70 per cent of the world's continental shelves consist of relict sediments which can be mined with little or no effect upon present beaches lying inshore of dredging sites. As shown by Table 2, sand and gravel is the second-most valuable marine mineral resource produced during 1964. The annual production has every prospect of increasing in the future as demands increase along the world's heavily populated coastal strips.

Heavy detrital minerals—For convenience in discussion, the economic heavy minerals that occur as detrital sands, or placers, can be separated into three groups on the basis of their specific gravity and toughness. These are heavy heavy minerals, light heavy minerals, and gems.

The heavy heavy minerals consist of gold, tin, and platinum, with specific gravities of 6.8 to 21. Because of their high specific gravity, heavy heavy minerals in economic deposits are nearly restricted to the vicinity of their primary sources in intrusive igneous and associated metamorphic rocks. About half of the economic placer deposits lie within 15 km of the sources; with rare exceptions, therefore, the placers are restricted to streams. One exception was the gold in present and raised ancient beaches that lay near the primary source at Nome, Alaska. Explorations for nearby submerged ancient beaches are taking place now, and if these deposits contain enough gold to exceed the greater costs of offshore than of onshore mining and concentrating, they may be worked in a few years. Production of gold from other beaches of the world is negligible, and production even from stream placers amounts to only 11 per cent of the total $1.3 billion annual production (Table 2), mostly from lodes on land. Platinum is similar to gold in its occurrence, but is relatively minor in quantity.

Tin, the last heavy heavy mineral, is more restricted in distance of transportation from its sources than is gold, because it tends to break rather than to bend upon impact. About 75 per cent of the world's $460 million annual production of tin is from stream placers. In Malaysia, Thailand, and Indonesia these placers continue beneath the sea as now-submerged former stream channels, but the value of the production from the sea floor was only $5 million in 1964, about one per cent of the total production of tin. Additional deposits probably are present on the sea floor, especially off Indonesia, and they may be mined in the near future.

The light heavy minerals consist chiefly of ilmenite and rutile (both are titanium species), zircon, monazite, and magnetite. Their specific gravities cover a narrow range from 4.2 to 5.3. Their unit value ($20 to $260 per ton) is much less than that of heavy heavy minerals, and although they are concentrated by streams, the stream deposits are too small to be economic. These minerals require the high energy environment of the ocean shore (as provided by waves) to achieve satisfactory separation from the accompanying quartz and feldspar and accumulation of large enough deposits to be mined economically. The production value of the beach deposits during 1964 totalled about $35 million. Land production for all except magnetite was only $48 million, so the light heavy minerals do not have an outstanding future potential for sea floor operations. Sea-floor production of magnetite, the iron mineral, is faced with decreasing demand, increasing costs, and is not very desirable in view of its content of titanium. The low unit value of all light heavy minerals, coupled with the greater cost of offshore than of beach mining indicates that a search for offshore submerged deposits is unlikely to discover deposits rich enough or large enough to be mined profitably. Monazite, the rare earth mineral, may be an exception because its unit value, $260 per ton, is much higher than those for the other minerals,

The last group of heavy minerals, gems, have specific gravities of 2.9 to 4.1. It is dominated by diamonds. Other gems such as sapphires and rubies are so fragile that production is almost entirely from streams, although production statistics are scant. About 90 per cent of the annual $284 million value of diamond production is also from streams or from raised beaches now on land. Only $4 million worth was produced from the sea floor beyond the modern beach off Southwest Africa, and this was reported to have cost more than the worth of the diamonds. A large increase in offshore production is considered highly unlikely using current techniques.

ORGANIC DEPOSITS

Deposits of organic origin are ones that are direct products or by-products of life processes. Oil, gas, and coal are good examples. Shells also are a direct product of life processes, but for convenience they were discussed in the section on detrital sand and gravel. Sulfur and several other materials are byproducts of the activities of organisms and will be considered later in this section.

Oil and gas—Most important of the organic minerals extracted from the sea floor are petroleum and natural gas. The oil and gas of the world are products of a long and inefficient series of transformations of energy. Each year about 1×10^{21} kilogram calories of energy reaches the earth from the sun. Some of it is used in photosynthesis that produces organic material which would be equivalent to 4×10^{17} kg cal if it were to be completely oxidized. Most of the organic matter is oxidized, but some of it becomes buried in the sediments, an amount equal to about 7×10^{14} kg cal. Oxidation continues in the sediments with preferential loss of proteins and carbohydrates, leaving lipids somewhat concentrated as hydrocarbons and more resistant complexes. Estimates of the total reserves of oil and gas, and the knowledge that they accumulated during about 500 million years, yields an average annual rate of accumulation of oil and gas equivalent to about 1×10^{10} kg cal. Thus the annual increment is only about 1×10^{-11}th of the influx of energy to the earth from the sun. The rate of extraction of oil and gas by man is rapid, 3×10^{16} kg cal per year from the entire world, or about three million times faster than it accumulated. Man is far more efficient in extracting and using oil and gas than is nature in providing it.

In an effort to further increase his production of oil and gas man has turned to the sea floor in his search for new sources beyond those that have been found on land. As a result, offshore production has increased from an almost negligible amount two decades ago to about one-sixth of the total world production in 1964, 1×10^{10} 42-gallon barrels plus about 5×10^{13} cubic feet of natural gas. As shown by Table 2, the value of offshore production during 1967 was about $800 million off the United States and about $3600 million for the sea floor of the entire world. A steady increase of the United States production reached more than $1300 million during 1967. The great production from the sea floor is from the continental shelves, many of which consist of huge

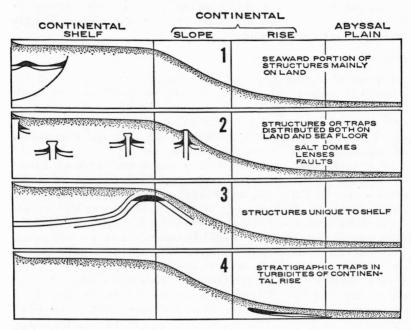

FIGURE 2.   *Types of Oil Traps or Structures on the Sea Floor. The sequence from top to bottom represents accumulations of oil and gas at progressively greater depth and distance from land, resulting in progressively lesser understanding and exploitation.*

piles of sediments that are dominated by Cenozoic and Cretaceous strata (dating from as far back as 135 million years ago). These strata contain source beds (usually organic-rich shales), reservoir beds (usually sandstones), and impervious caps (usually tight shales), and many structural traps and stratigraphic traps (Fig. 2). Moreover, the beds that are thin and barren on land commonly are thicker and richer offshore.

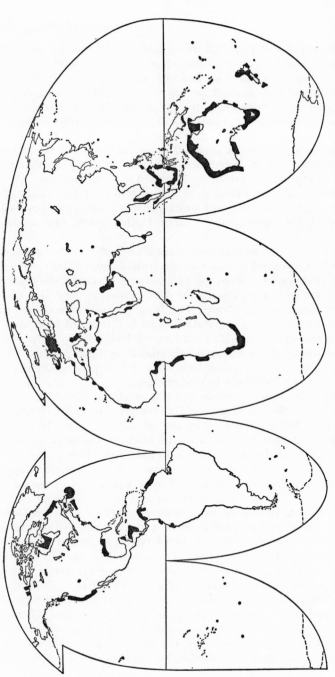

FIGURE 3. *Areas of the Continental Shelf for Which Permits to Explore for Oil and Gas Had Been Issued by Adjacent Countries up to 1967.*

A good example is provided by Australia, which until a few years ago had no production on land but whose peripheral shelf has now been almost completely leased for offshore exploration and drilling (Fig. 3). Offshore regions in most of the rest of the world are being actively investigated for their potential oil and gas supplies. The major sea-floor production is from the Persian Gulf, Lake Maracaibo, and off Louisiana, each of which are in the million barrel per day category. Other important production is from off California, with rising production from Alaska and the North Sea, and promise in many other regions. The chief areas that are being by-passed are the Arctic and Antarctic (rigorous climate and thick drift ice), eastern Asia (political and military problems), central and southern South America (political and geological limitations), and eastern United States (not opened for leasing).

Some idea of the scale of operations is indicated by the investment of $10 billion by the oil industry off the United States alone during the 12 year period 1953–64. Even the tax revenues derived from offshore oil and gas are very large. During the same period the total U.S. and state revenue from bonuses (leases) and from production revenues was $3 billion. Increase in subsequent revenues is illustrated by a single sale of $510 million for undrilled sea floor off Louisiana in 1967, and $603 million for similar sea floor off California in 1968. In this sale, bids reached $11,374 per acre off California. When production begins the tax royalties probably will be commensurate.

Little more than a decade ago the maximum depth of water for offshore oil wells was 25 meters. Today wells approach, but few exceed 200 meters. During the 1968 leasing off California few blocks deeper than 200 meters were ignored in the bidding, and most areas deeper than 400 meters that were offered brought bids. The interest in deep-water drilling is due, of course, to new methods of drilling and well completion that now are considered to be economical by the oil industry. These include the use of robots and deep saturating diving by man, as well as improvements in remote handling of drilling tools. In short, the depths that are of interest to the oil industry are increasing rapidly. Eventually the depths of effective production may even be adequate for exploitation of the continental rise that lies beyond the continental slope and is generally deeper than 3000 meters. These are the largest sedimentary features of the world, huge alluvial-fan-like piles of sediment that surround the continents and consist largely of debris eroded from them during 135 million or more years. Their upper parts are believed to consist of irregularly alternating bids of organic-rich sediment that has slid from the continental slopes, and beds of sand that were deposited by rapidly-flowing sediment-laden masses of water termed turbidity currents. If future drilling confirms the presence of oil and gas in the sands, we may have discovered the world's greatest supplies of fossil fuel. Some idea of the demand for future fuel supplies is indicated by Table 4, a projection for the United States alone by the

TABLE 4. *Consumption of Energy in the United States* (10^{15} kg cal)

	1947	1965	1985
Natural Gas	1.12	4.10	9.74
Petroleum	2.76	5.96	11.98
Coal	3.81	2.95	5.82
Water Power	0.07	0.16	0.34
Nuclear	0.00	0.01	2.22
Totals	7.76	13.18	30.10

Oil and Gas Journal, indicating an approximate doubling every two decades. Although the total oil and gas produced in the United States is expected to double during the next two decades, the proportion from offshore sources probably will also double, to an offshore production of at least four times the present rate.

Sulfur—The byproduct of organic activity having the greatest annual value is the sulfur that is closely associated with salt domes of the Gulf Coast of the United States. This sulfur is deposited by certain bacteria that are capable of using the sulfate ion in gypsum and anhydrite as an oxidizing agent for organic matter. Gypsum and anhydrite are minerals that are formed by solar evaporation of sea water, and both are associated with halite (common table salt). Where halite occurs in thick beds, its low specific gravity (about 2.3) permits it to rise hundreds or thousands of meters through overlying denser strata in the form known as salt domes (Fig. 2). When the halite reaches the ground surface or even the zone of circulating ground water, it dissolves and leaves a surface concentration of relatively insoluble minerals. These minerals include gypsum and anhydrite, which become what is known as caprock on the salt domes. Given enough time, the sulfate-reducing bacteria convert much of this caprock to elemental sulfur. Salt domes that do not rise high enough have no gypsum or anhydrite concentration, and thus no sulfur deposit; instead, they may contain highly soluble potash minerals that are essentially absent from salt domes that rise to near the ground surface on land or on the formerly exposed continental shelf. If the domes are very old, even the sulfur may have dissolved away; thus perhaps sulfur characterizes only salt domes that are of moderate age.

Initial discoveries of sulfur on salt domes were made accidentally during the drilling for oil known to occupy some of the sandy strata tilted by the upward movement of salt domes. Its recovery was found to be very simple and cheap. In the Frasch process one merely pumps hot water and air down through an inner pipe and recovers the froth of water, air, and melted sulfur through the annular space between the inner and an outer pipe. Production of sulfur from the outer continental shelf (federal jurisdiction) off Louisiana amounted to 635,000 tons in 1964 at $20 per ton, or about 10 per cent of total U.S. production of sulfur. Additional sulfur was imported by the United States, indicating that a market is available for additional sulfur from offshore sites.

Although not an organic material, some salt is also produced from offshore salt domes. In 1964 the quantity was only 200,000 tons at $6 per ton, less than 1 per cent of the total production of salt in the United States.

Coal—Paralleling the development of oil and gas mainly from marine plants is coal that formed from land plants. During the past as now, land plants store enormous quantities of energy as cellulose during their life spans of generally 1 to 100 years; in contrast, planktonic marine plants store little but they rapidly reproduce themselves with generation times of only 0.001 to 0.1 year. The average annual productivity per unit area is similar in both environments. On their death the land plants become oxidized and return their organic components to the atmosphere except under conditions that largely exclude bacteria. These conditions are met beneath the water level of swamps where the high concentration of decomposition products can prevent further growth of most bacteria, and in cold regions where the low temperature slows bacterial activity. Coals containing logs and tree stumps are typical of former swamps, and tundra (herbs) peat is an example of cold climate preservation. Mining of coal on land is so highly mechanized that recovery reaches 5 tons per day per man in the United States in contrast to less than a ton for hand mining in many countries where capital is lacking or miners are conservative. In some coastal regions where coastal plains of thick sediments and where mountains of igneous and metamorphic rocks are lacking, the coal lies at depth not only beneath the land but also under the ocean. Mines developed on land have been extended several kilometers beneath the ocean, but for all practical purposes the mining is independent of the presence of the ocean, and undersea coal mining is a land activity. Perhaps the majority of such undersea mining takes place in England, Nova Scotia, and Japan. The quantity of coal so produced is perhaps 10 per cent of all coal, with an annual value of about $0.3 billion.

Associated with coal mines are accumulations of methane, the gas that is a common cause of explosions in mines and of asphyxiation of miners. This is the gas (of non-marine origin) that was discovered in strata beneath the North Sea, during the 1960s and constitutes a new source of power for bordering countries.

Other organic materials—In tropical regions calcareous deposits, other than the loose shells that were described with sand and gravel, are mined. These deposits include reef rock used for concrete aggregate, and beachrock that occurs in slabs locally used as building stone. About 80,000 tons of fine-grained aragonite (a biochemical calcium carbonate precipitate plus algal debris) were mined from the shallow reefs of the Bahama Islands, probably for cement or agricultural purposes. Collected by divers, hundreds of tons of coral and colorful shells of large mollusks are sold as decorations to tourists in tropical seaside towns. Lastly, the small red gem coral from the tropics is a jewelry item whose value ranks with that of amber that is washed ashore by storms in the Baltic Sea. Both have been collected and used in jewelry for thousands of years, so that their distribution pattern in debris of early cultures marks ancient trade routes. Altogether, these miscellaneous organic materials have an annual production value of probably less than $1 million per year.

MINERALS OF OTHER ORIGIN

Several minerals or materials of origin other than authigenic, detrital, or organic come to mind, although none is economically important as yet.

Ships—An estimated one million ships have sunk in the ocean during historical time, and even the annual peacetime rate has been reported to be nearly 1 per cent of total tonnage. None of the ships that sank in the deep sea and few of those that sank far beyond the shore zone on the continental shelf have been salvaged. In many instances (such as the *Andrea Doria*) cargoes and hulls are valuable, but costs of salvage are even greater. When uncertainties of weather and of insurance and state tax claims are added, most operations are impractical. The bulk of the tonnage is steel, chiefly valuable as scrap unless the ship is in good condition and of recent construction. The average price for steel scrap during 1964 was $34 per ton, from which must be subtracted not only the cost of salvage but that of cutting up and transportation. Most attempts at salvage have been highly selective, seeking gold, silver, military material, or achaeological materials. Gold is the objective of most treasure seekers, apparently in the belief that many old sunken ships carried quantities of gold for army pay or transport to Europe from

Aztec or Inca sources. Undoubtedly, the value of gold and silver that has been recovered is negligible compared with the cost of past searches and attempts at recovery. Archaeological salvage is becoming increasingly important and its publicity has unfortunately attracted salvagers to supply the market for artifacts; for example, ancient amphorae are reported to now have a value of $120 each and even nineteenth-century anchors are worth $250.

Ground water—Offshore springs of fresh water have been known for many millenia by fishermen and others. Such springs supplied the Phoenician city of Aradus on a rocky island off Syria; others in the Persian Gulf filled special Arab boats whose cargo of fresh water was sailed to shore and sold. A large spring off Crescent Beach, Florida, discharges so much fresh water that sea level above it has a visible hump. Other nearshore as well as shoreline springs occur along most coasts, as revealed by infrared photographs from aircraft. Sea-floor test wells that were drilled off Florida during 1965 by the Joint Oceanographic Institutions' Deep Earth Sampling program encountered fresh water in the interstices of Cenozoic strata beneath the continental shelf. One well 40 km from shore penetrated a bed about 120 meters below the sea floor that had a hydrostatic head of at least nine meters, as shown by the rise of water in the drill pipe. Clearly, many freshwater wells could be drilled on the continental shelf; however, the cost of pipe lines and pumping the water to shore probably make this source uneconomic in comparison with other sources. Unfortunately, in the arid regions where the water is most wanted, the strata beneath the shelf probably contain little fresh water.

Water wells have been drilled on land to supply many coastal cities. Overpumping of these wells far beyond the rate of natural recharge has lowered the water table as much as 30 meters below sea level. With the lowering of the water table, the water in the strata beneath the continental shelf flows landward. In semiarid southern California this landward flow has permitted sea water to reach the wells, which then had to be abandoned. Expensive subsurface dams of mud and of artificially recharged fresh water were built between the shore and some wells in Los Angeles to impede and delay the approach of sea water. Obviously, in such areas the continental shelf is not a source of new supplies of fresh water. Overpumping of wells in the coastal region of southeastern United States has caused similar lowerings of the water table, or of water pressure, but the landsward flow of water beneath the shelf has not yet affected the salinity of the well water. The shelf is so wide and its content of fresh water is so great, that the approaching interface with sea water is still far offshore and its arrival may be hundreds of years away. Accordingly, the Atlantic coastal wells are producing water from beneath the ocean in much the same way that some coal mines on land produce coal from beneath the ocean. Probably several tens of million dollars worth of fresh water each year is extracted from beneath the sea floor in this way.

Red Sea sediments—Oceanographic expeditions to the Red Sea since 1959 have discovered and mapped several large depressions that contain hot brine below depths of about 2000 meters. Measured temperatures of the brine are about 56°C, and salinities are about 310 grams per kilogram, nearly ten times as salty as ordinary sea water. Cores have shown the presence of varicolored sediments at least 9 meters thick beneath the brine in areas that total about 70 km². The sediments are rich in certain metals, with variations related to the several facies that were cored. Studies by James L. Bischoff and Frank T. Manheim yield the following weighted average percentages of the more valuable metals in dried brine-free sediment: zinc, 4.6; copper, 1.8; lead, 0.14; silver, 0.006; and gold, 6×10^{-5}. Taking into account these concentrations and the area covered by the deposit, and assuming a thickness of 10 meters, the authors estimate the value of the deposit at about \$2 billion. On a unit basis the value is about \$5 per cubic meter, or \$28 per ton of brine-free sediment. Copper constitutes more than half of the total value. Thicknesses are greater than ten meters, and they may reach 90 meters according to some geophysical measurements, but nothing is known of the composition of the sediments below nine meters. The total value of the metals in the deposit may far exceed the estimate, but the sediment has not yet been mined and processed on a commercial basis. A favorable property is the fine-grained slurry character of the sediment, which probably will permit it to be pumped from the sea floor to a ship for processing or transportation.

This unique deposit is probably due to the escape of deep intergranular water heated by the geothermal gradient and by a mixture of water from magma that has intruded this tectonically active region. On land, similar solutions moving upward through openings in the rock form metalliferous vein deposits as they cool and reach depths of lower pressure. When the solutions escape into the bottom of the Red Sea, the hydrostatic pressure of overlying water is great and cooling is slow, but there are no walls to confine the deposition of minerals to narrow veins. The metals in the escaping water spread throughout the accumulated brine and, eventually, they are deposited as disseminated sulfides. In effect, the Red Sea has taken the place of the upper layers of rock on land and prevented the deposition of ores as shallow or moderate-depth veins.

Chemical Resources

Every cubic kilometer of sea water contains about 40 million tons of dissolved solids having a value of more than $1 billion if extracted. The two most abundant elements, sodium and chlorine, have been extracted for at least five thousand years as impure halite (common salt) through solar evaporation. In the United States during 1964 an estimated 2 million tons of salt having a value of about $11 million were produced in this way. Most of it is used for snow and ice removal, water softening, and refrigeration; the purer forms are used in the chemical industry. The world production of salt by evaporation of sea water is about 35 million tons annually, about one-third of the total world production of salt from all sources, mainly bedded rock salt.

The third most abundant element in sea water, magnesium, is removed in several processing plants in Texas. The total value of the extracted magnesium and its compounds is reported to be about $65 million per year.

Bromine also is extracted from sea water at the Texas plants at a rate of about $23 million per year. About twice as much comes from oil-field brines on land.

Considerable mention has been made of dissolved gold in sea water. In fact, the famous Meteor expedition of the 1920's was organized largely in response to the German chemist Fritz Haber's belief that the war debt might be repaid with gold extracted from sea water. However, his analyses of many thousands of water samples showed average values of less than 0.001 mg of gold per ton of sea water. Although several million dollars have been spent altogether on developing processes, the total quantity of gold that has been extracted reportedly is worth less than $0.01. Even if total extraction were successful, the value of the gold would be insufficient even to pay for pumping the water.

Sea water is a source not only of many elements but also of fresh water. In arid regions where fresh water from other sources is lacking, it can be produced from sea water by distillation, freezing, ion exchange, and semi-permeable membranes that make use of osmosis or electro-dialysis. Distillation appears to be the most economic process through many ingenious variations. All of the methods require the addition of outside energy. Solar energy is inefficient because of its low level and the large capital investment in area and equipment required to collect the energy. Fossil fuels are used in many small installations at a cost of about $2 per 1000 gallons. Atomic energy may be cheaper only in terms of free (subsidized) sources and low volume (low cost) transportation of the energy. Present levels are reported to be $0.85 per

1000 gallons. This is still about double the rate paid for municipal water after distribution, and it is more than 20 times the cost of pumping and treating fresh water from lakes or wells. Increased demand for water with dwindling surface and underground supplies undoubtedly will force a more realistic evaluation of water as a "free" commodity. The present domestic use of water, which amounts to about 100 gallons per capita per day, might be drastically reduced if the cost to the consumer were increased tenfold.

Living Marine Resources

From time immemorial man has depended upon the living resources of the sea for part of his food supply. The amount of sea food in the diet is extremely variable and depends not only upon availability but also upon the culture of the people. For example, it is clear that some American Indians spent their summers at the seashore. Studies of their kitchen middens indicate that they enjoyed a varied and abundant sea food diet. The Eskimo of Greenland, however, consider fishing to be "women's work" and they eat fish rarely and only when the seal, walrus, and polar bears are scarce. The Scandinavian people, particularly those living along the coast of Norway, have always been heavy consumers of sea food, and in the Far East sea food provides more than half of the annual supply of animal protein for the population.

Mankind is now facing serious problems of rapid population expansion. Even today many people are undernourished or improperly nourished, and this problem is certain to be aggravated as the population expands. Oceanographers are frequently asked whether these teeming millions can be fed by the produce of the sea. The answers have ranged from wildly optimistic overestimates to pessimistic fears that we are already overexploiting our marine resources and that further uncontrolled exploitation may lead to disaster. In the following section, we therefore assess the present supply of food resources from the sea and attempt to evaluate various predictions which have been made concerning the potential.

THE NEED FOR ANIMAL PROTEIN

First, however, it should be emphasized that marine food resources hold practical potential as animal protein, but not as vegetable material. The production of plant life in the oceans is great and has been variously estimated as equal to or in excess of the production of plant life on land, even when the terrestrial production includes the forests which are not currently available as food. Plant life in the oceans, however, consists almost exclusively of microscopic algae, the phytoplankton, which are thinly dispersed throughout a considerable depth of the water column. Harvesting them in quantity is impractical, because, even under favorable growth conditions in the sea, one would have to filter a million pounds of sea water to obtain a pound of the plankton life which it contains. It is true that one finds dense bands of sea weeds along the shore, but the water shallow enough for the growth of attached algae is less than one per cent of the ocean's surface area, and the rate of production of plant material by these larger algae is a small part of the total production in the sea. Harvesting the plant production of the oceans is, thus, not a practical solution to man's hunger even though the total production of organic matter by these microscopic plants is great.

Protein deficiency is, however, one of the most serious aspects of malnutrition in the world population. Ten amino acids, the building blocks of proteins, are essential for human nutrition. Many vegetable diets fail to supply the amount of protein needed and some diets are deficient in one or another of these ten essential amino acids. These deficiencies are most pronounced when the population lives on a diet which is dominated by one staple crop. Approximately 1.5 billion persons, largely in tropical and sub-tropical areas, live on such limited diets. Even though adequate calories may be supplied, the lack of essential amino acids and vitamins may produce chronic debilitation as a result of malnutrition.

Chronic protein deficiency is a leading cause of death in the early years of life, and it limits the life span and productive capacity of adults. It will be essential to improve the nutrition of billions of people before they can enjoy the abundance and benefits of the twentieth century. A more diverse vegetable diet could be provided, but these deficiencies can most easily be overcome by supplying a supplement of animal protein to the diet. A daily supplement of 10–20 grams of animal protein, a mere 8–16 pounds of animal protein annually, would suffice to overcome the debilitating effects of protein deficiency. The type of animal protein is of little consequence; sea food will serve just as well as beef, pork or chicken. It is in terms of supplying the need for animal protein that marine resources offer the greatest promise for the future.

Fish meal and protein concentrate—Part of the marine fisheries harvest is not eaten directly by man, but is used for the production of high protein food supplements for poultry and livestock. Full utilization of all species of fish in an exploited area can be achieved by reserving the more desirable species for human consumption and using the less desirable, so-called trash fish, for the production of fish meal, fish oil and other industrial products. About 40 per cent of the U.S.

catch was used for these purposes in 1966. The dangers of spoilage, always present with fresh fish, and the need for elaborate refrigeration for frozen products are avoided. From the point of view of human nutrition, however, this is wasteful, since some of the protein in fish is lost in its conversion to poultry or livestock protein.

The Bureau of Commercial Fisheries has developed a process for the production of a marine protein concentrate from various species of hake, a fish little used in the U.S. markets. A ton of hake yields 320 pounds of concentrate containing 250 pounds of protein at an estimated cost of 25 cents per pound. AID has been assigned the lead agency role in developing a new "Food-from-the-Sea" program, and has established as goals, during the next five years, the development of commercial processes for the production of fish protein concentrate, (FPC), the evaluation and development of a market for FPC in at least one protein deficient country and the establishment of a viable commercial production system in at least one protein deficient country. Increasing the available supply of fish will, necessarily, be an important part of this program.

There are, of course, sociological and cultural problems to be solved in introducing a new food product. FPC is bacteriologically and biochemically safe and stable, highly nutritious and almost tasteless and odorless. It can easily be added to a number of prepared foods, such as bread or cereals, which are consumed in developing countries. Ten grams of FPC would provide enough animal protein to meet the daily needs of a growing child at a cost of about two dollars per year. The introduction of FPC in poorly nourished countries offers promise of solving some of the serious problems of protein malnutrition.

THE HARVEST FROM THE SEA

The harvest of the food resources of the sea has increased since World War II at a rate which considerably exceeds the rate of growth of human populations. The data shown in Figure 4 indicate that from 1955 to 1965 the commercial catch of fish increased at a compounded rate of more than 6 per cent per year.[1] In part, this large increase resulted from exploiting fish stocks in highly productive areas of the oceans which had not been previously harvested. An example of this was the anchovy fisheries off the coast of Peru which increased the

---

[1] The sport fishery catch in U.S. coastal and marine waters in 1960 was estimated at about 10 per cent of the U.S. commercial catch in that year. *Sport Fishing Today and Tomorrow* (Bureau of Sports Fisheries and Wildlife, 1960), 127 pp. Report to Outdoor Recreation Resources Review Commission, ORRRC Study Report 7. Adequate statistics are not available to permit evaluation of the non-commercial catch on a world-wide basis.

Peruvian contribution to the world harvest of fish from less than one
billion pounds to a maximum of over 20 billion pounds annually. The
increase was also due, in part, to the introduction of modern fishing
methods such as factory ships and catchers. In 1968, these were being
used extensively by the Soviet Union which had about doubled its
catch from 1955 to 1965. While the world harvest of marine products

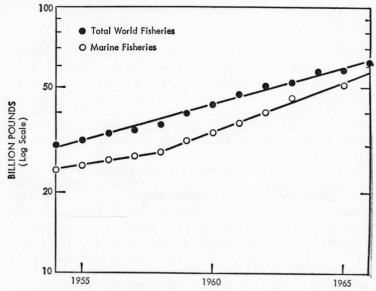

FIGURE 4. *Annual Commercial World Catch of Fish and Shellfish.*

nearly doubled during this time, the catch by U.S. fishermen remained
nearly constant at about six billion pounds per year. In the mid-1950's,
the U.S. catch was second only to that of Japan. Because of increased
harvesting by other nations, the United States dropped to sixth place
by 1966. Peru, Japan, Mainland China, the Soviet Union, and Norway
increased their landings sharply in the middle 1960's so that each of
these nations was harvesting more from the sea than the United States.

THE POTENTIAL HARVEST

The potential of the marine fisheries has historically been grossly
underestimated by the fisheries experts in the past as M. B. Schaefer
has pointed out.[2] Harold Thompson, at a U.N. Conference at Lake,

[2] Milner B. Shaefer, "The Potential Harvest of the Sea," *Transactions of the
American Fisheries Society,* 94, No. 2 (April 1965), 123–28.

Success, New York, in 1949, estimated that the fisheries catch could be increased by four million tons over pre-war production, to give a harvest of about 22 million tons.[3] This level of production was exceeded by the marine fisheries alone within a year of publication of the prediction. In 1953 the fisheries division, FAO, concluded that world fish production could be doubled without detriment to the resource and indicated a total catch of 34 million tons might be achieved by 1960.[4] The world catch exceeded this estimate by 1956 and the

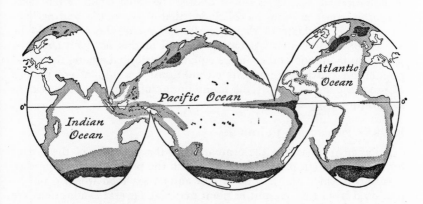

FIGURE 5. *Schematic Representation of the Probable Relative Plant Productivity of Ocean Areas. Black indicates very productive areas, light shading moderately productive regions.*

marine commercial catch exceeded it in 1960. Graham and Edwards (1962) recognized the fact that fish landings from the ocean had doubled during the previous decade and estimated the potential harvest at 55 million tons. The marine catch has not yet exceeded this estimate, but the world catch, including about 11 per cent of commercially caught fresh water fish, exceeded it in 1965.[5] Meseck (1962) estimated that an increase to 100 million tons by the end of this cen-

[3] Harold Thompson, "Latent Fishery Resources and Means for Their Development," *Proceedings United Nations Conference Conservation and Utilization of Resources* (New York: United Nations, 1951), 7:28–38.

[4] Fisheries Division, FAO, "Improving the Fisheries Contribution to World Food Supply," (Rome: Food and Agriculture Organization of United Nations, Fisheries Bulletin, 1953), 6: 159–91.

[5] Herbert W. Graham and Robert L. Edwards, "The World Biomass of Marine Fishes," in *Fish in Nutrition,* eds. Eirik Heen and Rudolf Kreuzer, First International Conference Fish in Nutrition (London: Fishing News Books Ltd., 1962), pp. 3–8.

tury might be achieved.[6] Extrapolation of the world catch statistics in Figure 5 would suggest that this level for the commercial catch will be reached in 1974 if the growth of the world fisheries continues at the present rate. Schaefer (1965) emphasized that we are not harvesting all of the fish available even in heavily fished areas and that new stocks of fish, like the Peruvian anchovy, will be discovered and exploited in other parts of the world. He estimated that harvesting all of the fish in presently fished areas might double the commercial catch, and that exploitation of new areas might double the catch again. From these and other considerations he concluded that a reasonable, and perhaps conservative, estimate of the potential harvest of the sea should be about 200 million tons. Assuming that all of this sea food could be used as human food and could be equally distributed among the world population (obviously impossible conditions) it would, at 250 pounds of protein per ton, supply the minimum animal protein requirement for 5 billion people.

PRIMARY PRODUCTION IN THE SEA

Another approach to the evaluation of the potential of the oceans for the production of food is to start with the primary (plant) production and to calculate the quantity of animal sea food which could be produced from this amount of plant material. Several assumptions are required in order to make the calculation and the basic information is by no means completely accurate. This kind of a computation can, therefore, be biased so as to prove almost any point that the author wishes to establish, but it can give an upper limit to the natural production of food if we continue to depend upon the harvest of whatever the bounty of nature provides.

The rate of plant production varies widely in different parts of the ocean, as shown in Figure 5 (Sverdrup, 1955).[7] Some estimates of the rates of production in various parts of the world oceans are given in Table 5. The shaded areas in Figure 5 are indicative of high plant production. All of these areas have mechanisms to enrich the surface water with water from greater depths, where the nutrient concentration is higher. For example, off the west coast of continents, such as the coast of Africa or South America, persistent trade winds move the near-

   [6] G. Meseck, "Importance of Fisheries Production and Utilization in the Food Economy," in *Fish in Nutrition*, eds. Eirik Heen and Rudolf Kreuzer, First International Conference Fish in Nutrition (London: Fishing News Books Ltd., 1962), pp. 23–37.
   [7] H. V. Sverdrup, "The Place of Physical Oceanography in Oceanographic Research," *Journal of Marine Research* (New Haven: Sears Foundation for Marine Research, Yale University, 1955), 14: 287–94.

TABLE 5. *Some Estimates of the Photosynthetic Fixation of Carbon by Marine Phytoplankton* (Ryther, 1963)

Area	Carbon Fixation		
	gC/m²/day	gC/m²/year	Fresh wt.** lbs/acre/year
Tropical Areas			
Open ocean waters	0.05–0.15	18–55*	1600–4900
Equatorial Pacific	0.50	180*	16060
Equatorial Indian	0.20–0.25	73–90*	6513–8030
Upwelling Areas	0.50–1.00	180–360*	16060–32120
Sargasso Sea	0.10–0.89	72	6420
Temperate Areas			
Continental Shelf off			
New York	0.33 (mean)	120	10710
Fladen Ground, North Sea		57–82	5085–7320
Kuroshio Current	0.05–0.10	18–36*	1600–3200
Oyashio Current	0.25–0.50	?	–
Arctic Ocean	0.005–0.024	1	89
All oceans estimated mean: (361.1 × 10⁶km²)	0.137	50	4460

* Seasonal cycle assumed negligible; annual production computed from daily rates.
** gC/m²/yr. × 8.922 = lb. C/acre/year. This is multiplied by 10 to give the approximate fresh weight of plant material.

surface waters offshore and permit upwelling of waters from intermediate depths. In the southern ocean there is a major current flowing completely around the Antarctic Continent, and associated with this current is a divergence which again brings nutrient-rich waters close to the surface. The vertical turbulence which occurs at current fronts, and particularly between two opposing current systems, such as is found in the equatorial oceans, can also fertilize the surface waters and increase the rate of plant production. The continental shelves and great fishing banks, like Georges Banks and the Grand Banks in the North Atlantic, are comparatively shallow areas where wind stirring and tidal mixing enrich the surface waters and increase the productivity. The effect of river water carrying nutrients into the sea is important in coastal areas and in semi-confined bodies of water such as the Gulf of Mexico. However, in terms of the total oceanic production, river drainage adds only about 1 per cent of the total nutrient requirement each year. Thus, while river drainage is locally very important, its value to the productivity of the sea has been greatly over-emphasized by some. Excluding the Arctic, where ice and snow cover drastically limit the penetration of light, the estimates of oceanic production show a range of about fifty-fold, with the lower values being comparable to plant production on deserts and the higher values being comparable to the rate of production of good farm land.

The great variability in the estimates of production and the fact that seasonal studies have been made in very few parts of the world's oceans means that assigning a value for total plant production is little better than an educated guess. Using a conservative estimate of average production of 50 gC/m^2/year an estimate of about 20 billion tons of carbon incorporated into living plant material annually in the world ocean is obtained. The fresh weight of living material, the units in which our fisheries catches are reported, would be about 10 times this quantity, or 200 billion tons a year. Comparison of this value with the data in Figure 4 shows that, today, we are harvesting only about 0.03 per cent of the annual productivity of the oceans.

THE CYCLE OF LIFE IN THE SEA

The concentration of plant material is so sparse in the ocean that about a million pounds of sea water has to be filtered in order to obtain a pound of living plant material. Natural processes in the ocean concentrate this living material into progressively larger "packages" to produce, ultimately, organisms of a size which are useful and economical to capture for human food. These processes begin when herbivores—small animals, frequently invertebrates—strain the microscopic phytoplankton from the water and convert the plants to animal material. Herbivores are eaten by carnivores, which themselves form the food for larger organisms. Each step in this process involves a loss of food material and energy since each organism requires part of the food eaten for life processes and for the energy expended in capturing food. The efficiency of conversion of food into new living material is variable and is generally higher in the young stages of organisms, when growth is rapid, and approaches zero in the fully grown adult where all of the food eaten may be required to maintain the organism at a fixed size without further growth. As a rough approximation, an average efficiency of 10 per cent conversion of food to new animal matter may be expected at each new step in the process. It is clear that the number of steps (called trophic levels) involved in producing the organism finally harvested will set a maximum limit to the total quantity of that organism which can be produced in any marine environment.

Some of the marine products which we harvest are herbivores, and these have the maximum potential for animal production in any given area. Examples of herbivores are small fish such as the anchovy, which is an important part of the rapidly expanding fisheries off Peru, and shellfish such as oysters, clams and mussels, which can be enormously productive under the proper conditions. Most of our marine products are, however, carnivores occupying higher trophic levels. On the basis of an average 10 per cent efficiency at each trophic level, to harvest the first stage carnivore, which is two levels removed from the phytoplankton, would be to harvest 1 per cent of the annual phytoplankton production. The proportion which can be harvested decreases with each progressive step of the food chain. Currently about 40 per cent of the world fisheries harvest consists of small fishes, such as the herring, sardine, and anchovy, or of mollusks or crustaceans. These forms feed on a mixed diet of phytoplankton and smaller zooplankton and consequently their potential production would lie at about five per cent of the total plant production of the area. Schaefer (1965) assumes that the harvest is taken, on the average, at the third trophic level and on this basis computes that the limit of harvest from the sea might reach approximately 0.1 per cent of plant production or about 200 million tons annually. Chapman (1965)[8] apparently believes that the harvest could be made at a lower trophic level since he concludes that the ocean is producing, each year, about 2 billion tons of animals that are "large enough and useful enough to form the basis for practical commercial harvesting." Since we are currently harvesting only about three per cent of this quantity the rest have been eaten by marine forms or have died, decayed and returned to the web of life in the ocean. Chapman also states that the probable error of his calculation is greater than the fraction of the total animal population which is now caught and used by man.

AQUACULTURE

All of the preceding discussion has been based upon the premise that we "let nature take its course" and that man merely hunts for and harvests those organisms which are easy to find and economical to harvest—a premise that man rejected several thousand years ago in his utilization of the land areas of the world. On cultivated land covering large areas of the earth we have eliminated undesirable species and replaced them with plants and animals which man finds agreeable and useful. How much could the seas produce if aquaculture where studied and pursued with the vigor which has characterized our agricultural program?

Aquaculture has progressed more rapidly in other parts of the world than it has in the United States. Here, research on marine aquaculture

[8] Wilbert M. Chapman, "Food from the Sea," address before Agricultural Research Institute, National Academy of Science, Washington, D.C., 1965 (Unpublished).

is essentially non-existent, except for limited studies on oysters, clams, and shrimp. The actual practice of aquaculture is limited largely to oyster culture, which involves transplanting the seed oysters to areas where the growth rate is better, and to clam purification which involves transplanting clams from polluted waters where shellfishing is prohibited to clean waters where they can grow and purify themselves. Stocking fresh waters with small fish has been practiced for many years but only in the last few decades has this been done with enough understanding of the environment and of natural processes so that it is reasonably assured of success. In a few cases, species have been transplanted to areas where they were previously not found, such as the Atlantic striped bass which is now approaching abundance in some parts of the Pacific Northwest and the Japanese oyster which has also been introduced in our Pacific waters.

Theoretically, at least, our estuaries and coastal waters could be managed as intensively as we manage our farm lands and the potential harvest from these areas could be enormously increased. Unfortunately these same waters are also being used for the disposal of the wastes of our modern civilization and they are over-fertilized with sewage so that obnoxious and undesirable species of algae, which are inedible or undigestible by the herbivores, have frequently replaced the natural populations. In our aquatic environment we are deliberately and carelessly fostering the growth of these "weeds," a practice which we assiduously avoid on our farm lands. Intelligent disposal of the waste products of our technology could, conceivably, increase the production of desirable marine products and transform what is now a public health hazard and national disgrace into a valuable asset for mankind.

Aquaculture as it is practiced in many parts of the world is far more productive of desirable marine protein resources than the same area would be if left to natural processes, as shown by the data in Table 6. A comparison of the world marine fish harvest (shown in Figure 4) and the approximately 90 billion acres of sea-surface area indicates that we are harvesting a rough average of about one pound per acre from the oceans. The importance of the continental shelves has been emphasized previously, and Graham and Edwards in 1962 estimated that the catch of fish per unit area of productive continental shelf area on the eastern coast of the United States was about twenty pounds per acre. Schaefer (1965) estimated that the fisheries off the coast of Peru and northern Chile are now producing at the rate of over 400 pounds per acre. Since the fisheries of the North American Atlantic Continental Shelf contain primarily carnivorous forms and the Peruvian fishery is both in an unusually rich area and dependent upon the anchovy, a herbivore of the first trophic level, this difference in production would be expected. The

TABLE 6. *Aquaculture—Production of Animals in Pounds per Acre*
(PSAC, 1966)*

	Animal	Yield pounds/acre
Unfertilized sea water ponds		
Philippines	milkfish	400–980
France	grey mullet	300
Java	milkfish	40–300
Indonesia	milkfish	140
"	prawns	46
"	wildfish	23
Fertilized sea water ponds		
Formosa	milkfish	1000
Fertilized Brackish Ponds		
Palestine (experimental)	carp	755–7970
" (commercial)	carp	356–4210
Oyster Culture (Ryther, 1968)		
U. S. Public Grounds (ave.)	oyster	6
U. S. Private Grounds	"	170–5000
France	"	320– 740
Australia	"	120–4400
Philippines (max.)	"	10000
Japan (max.)	"	50000
Land		
Cultivated Land	swine	450
Grassland	cattle	5–250

* President's Science Advisory Committee, *Effective Use of the Sea*. Report of the
Panel on Oceanography of the President's Science Advisory Committee, 1966. 144 pp.
U.S. Government Printing Office, Superintendent of Documents, Washington, D.C.
$.60.

data in Table 6 indicate that the productivity of unfertilized fish ponds
equals or exceeds these rates of production for the natural harvest, and
the fertilized fish ponds can exceed the natural production by as much
as twenty-fold. In Japan aquaculture has developed to the stage where
it is now producing 6 per cent of the total sea fisheries. However, this
six per cent consists of those species which are most desired and easily
marketed and therefore the value is 15 per cent of the value of the sea
fishery.

In the culture of shellfish, man can exploit several natural processes
in order to increase productivity. Oysters and mussels, which have been
successfully cultured, feed directly upon the phytoplankton and small

zooplankton and consequently can convert the maximum amount of plant material into animal material. They have the further advantage that they are stationary, living attached to surfaces, so that where the circulation is large they can utilize the production of plant material from a large area of the sea. For example, Hutchins and Deevey[9] found an increase in growth rate of the mussel by a factor of 2 to 4 as the mean current velocity increased from 0.41 to about 1 knot. This species can develop enormous populations in flowing streams of water such as the intake conduits of power plants, where it can be a serious problem.

The most effective means of oyster culture is to grow them either on stakes driven into the bottom or on ropes suspended from rafts. Both methods use the entire volume of the water, not only the part in proximity to the bottom. The raft system is the most effective since the oyster is isolated from some of the predators which crawl about on the bottom. Whereas oysters growing in beds on the bottom have yielded up to 600 pounds per acre, cultivation, using the raft method, has produced as much as 50,000 pounds per acre.

As pointed out in the PSAC report, the Public Health Service has estimated that there are about 10 million acres of estuarine waters that are suitable for shellfish production. It is informative to calculate the potential oyster production for this large area, though utilizing about 3 million acres of this total would require pollution abatement. Using the value for the minimum oyster production on U.S. private grounds in Table 6, our annual supply of oyster meats could be not 50,000 pounds as it was in 1966, but 1.7 billion pounds. This would equal 28 per cent of our total annual U.S. fish catch. The data in Table 6 indicate that the maximum yield could be many times greater than this.

It is clear that if the United States were farming the sea with the same intensity that we are farming the land the potential production of marine animal protein could be increased far above the natural rates of production which were estimated in the previous section. It may be of even greater importance to the United States to support the research and engineering which would enable us to assist protein deficient countries in the development of aquaculture on their own continental shelves and in their bays and estuaries.

INCREASING PLANT PRODUCTION

It is also possible that we could increase the production of the phytoplankton, at least in selected areas, by applying the knowledge that we already have about the cycle of life in the sea. We would need more

[9] Louis W. Hutchins and Edward S. Deevey, "Estimation and Prediction of the Weight and Thickness of Mussel Fouling Buoys," report, Woods Hole Oceanographic Institution to Bureau of Ships, April 19, 1944 (Unpublished).

information to be sure that the food produced as a result of this increased production would be of a kind which would be desirable. Our present information merely indicates that more living material would be produced, but we cannot predict whether or not it would be of the sort that man wants.

Two ways to increase the production of plant material are obvious and both of them depend upon increasing the fertility of the water. This we do on farm land by adding fertilizer, but this seems a wasteful and expensive way to do it in the oceans since the continuous motion of the water would dilute the added fertilizers and spread them widely with an unpredictable effect on the production. Adding fertilizers to confined ponds might be economically useful but in larger bodies of water better methods are available.

The growth of phytoplankton in temperate waters is limited, during the summer time, by the availability of nutrients. Plant growth removes almost completely the small amounts which are present in the surface waters at the start of the season. Enough sunlight for significant photosynthetic production of organic matter penetrates to a depth of only 100 meters or so even in the clearest ocean waters and photosynthesis is limited to a much shallower depth in coastal waters. The deep water is thus always richer in nutrients than the surface waters and, as discussed above, the richest parts of the ocean have a mechanism for the return of these nutrients to the surface. Additional mixing could be produced by various means in the head waters of an estuary and could increase the primary production of the entire estuarine system. This could be done, for example, by releasing the heated cooling water from nuclear or steam power plants at depths rather than at the surface. This heated water would rise to the surface entraining the nutrient-rich deep water in the process. One could thus employ the heat from these power plants in a beneficial way. We would begin thinking of this heat as an added natural resource rather than as a pollutant to be disposed of.

One could also make use of the fertilizing effects of domestic sewage. Here again this requires a complete reorientation of our thinking so that we consider this waste as a useful resource rather than as a pollutant to be disposed of in the cheapest way possible. Our present practice leads to overfertilization of the water, excessive growth of plants, and, when these die and decompose, to the complete removal of oxygen from the water. Deliberate addition of certain elements or organic compounds might be necessary to produce a naturally balanced fertilizer for the marine environment, but it is always essential that the quantity released in any given locality should not exceed the capacity of the natural populations to make use of it.

Sea water is a nicely balanced solution for plant production. Nitrogen and phosphorus are the elements which most commonly limit plant growth in the sea, though trace elements, such as cobalt and iron may be limiting under some conditions. Plant growth utilizes these essential elements in photosynthesis and releases oxygen, which escapes to the atmosphere since the process occurs in the near-surface waters. The balance is such that the decomposition of the organic matter which can be formed in a fertile sea water will utilize approximately the total oxygen contained in saturated sea water. Any substantial excess of organic matter leads to anaerobic conditions. Pollution may add organic matter directly or add essential elements released in treatment plants which stimulate growth of the natural populations. Over-fertilizing the sea by the disposal of sewage almost inevitably produces obnoxious effects. On the other hand, mixing the deep water into the surface waters will not develop obnoxious conditions since the balance with oxygen is maintained. The natural conditions in the sea thus set the known and identifiable limits to the concentration of pollutants which can be safely added to any body of water. If additions are kept within these narrow limits beneficial effects, specifically increased productivity, can be obtained; if these limits are exceeded the results will be disastrous. The situation is complex since conditions vary greatly from place to place. No casual rule of thumb will suffice and a scientific analysis of each locality will be necessary to assess properly the problem.

Using pollution so as to increase productivity can obviously not be done without an understanding of the problem, good management and the expenditure of a great deal of money. Some of this expenditure could well have an economic return if the changes are done wisely, so that obnoxious effects are avoided and man's harvest from the sea is increased.

SOME SOCIOLOGICAL AND POLITICAL PROBLEMS

A serious deterrent to the deliberate enhancement of marine production is the fact that the fish are common property; they belong to no one or to everyone, depending upon the point of view, until they are reduced to possession aboard a fishing vessel. A commercial enterprise in aquaculture will not be practical until the man who invests his funds in increasing the productivity of the ocean can be assured that he will reap the benefits. Two approaches have been made to the solution of this problem but neither one has, so far, been completely satisfactory.

Many nations of the world are now claiming exclusive fishing rights over much wider areas of the adjacent oceans than the part identified as their territorial limits. A summary of some of these claims is given in Table 7. These extended limits have not all been recognized. The

TABLE 7. *Breadth of Fishing Jurisdiction Claimed by Various Members of the United Nations.* (Where separate fishing limits are not claimed, extent of territorial waters is listed.)

3 miles	6 miles	12 miles		more than 12 miles
Australia	Ceylon (c)	Albania	Iraq	Argentina (200)
China	Dominican	Algeria	Ireland (b)	Cameroun (18)
Costa Rica	Republic	Belgium (b)	Italy (b)	Chile (200)
Cuba	Finland (4)	Brazil	Jamaica	Ecuador (200)
Gabon	Greece	Bulgaria	Kuwait	El Salvador (200)
Gambia	Haiti	Burma	Liberia	Guinea (130)
Ivory Coast	Israel	Cambodia (c)	Libya	India (100)
Japan	Lebanon	Canada	Malagasy	Indonesia (a)
Kenya	Maldive	Colombia	Republic	Korea (20–200) (c)
Malaysia	Islands	Cyprus	Mauritania	Nicaragua (200) (c)
Malta	Senegal	Dahomey	Mexico	Panama (200)
Poland	Somali	Denmark (b)	Morocco	Peru (200)
Trinidad	Republic	Greenland	Netherlands (b)	Philippines (a)
& Tobago		Faroe	New Zealand	
		Islands	Nigeria	
		Ethiopia	Norway	
		Federal Rep.	Pakistan (c)	
		of Germany (b)	Portugal (b)	
		France	Romania	
		Ghana (c)	Saudi	
		Guatemala	Arabia	
		Honduras	Sierra	
		Iceland	Leone	
		Iran	South Africa	
			Spain (b)	
			Sudan	
			Sweden (b)	
			Syria	
			Tanzania	
			Thailand	
			Togo	
			Tunisia (c)	
			Turkey	
			Ukrainian	
			U.S.S.R.	
			United Arab	
			Republic	
			United Kingdom (b)	
			United States of	
			America	
			Uruguay	
			Venezuela	
			Yemen	
			Yugoslavia (10)	
			Vietnam (20 km)	

(a) Archipelago theory—waters within straight lines joining appropriate points of outermost islands of the archipelago are considered internal waters.
(b) Parties to the European Fisheries Convention.
(c) Additional rights reserved for the continental shelf and superadjacent waters.

most common breadth of the zone of fisheries jurisdiction is now 12 miles and the parties to the European Fisheries Convention recognize the right of member nations to establish a three-mile exclusive fishing zone seaward of the three-mile territorial sea plus an additional six-mile fishing zone restricted to the Convention nations. Several countries claim rights to the continental shelf which varies in width from a few miles to 100 miles or more and the superadjacent waters. Still other countries claim fishing jurisdiction over waters which are well beyond the limits of the continental shelf, such as the claims of Peru, Chile and other nations for jurisdiction to a distance of 200 miles from the coast.

Even if these claims for jurisdiction over wide areas were commonly recognized, the basic problems in encouraging commercial participation in the development of new or increased living marine resources would not be solved. The old concept of the freedom of the seas is diametrically opposed to the improvement of marine food resources. Governments could, of course, undertake programs for improvement of resources over areas where the catch could be restricted to their own citizens. Fishermen, however, will remain hunters, rather than herders or farmers of the marine resources until the responsibility for the wise management of the living resources is clearly defined and the manager can reasonably expect to benefit from his efforts.

Another activity which has been growing rapidly in recent years is the increasing number of specialized intergovernmental fisheries commissions. The prototype for this type of commission, which is both governmental and scientific in structure is the International Council for the Exploration of the Sea. This was founded about the turn of the century. Initially its area of interest was limited to the North Sea, but this has now expanded to include most of the fisheries of the North Atlantic. Annual meetings have been held, except when prevented by wars. At the 55th Statutory Meeting in Hamburg in 1967 delegates attended from seventeen nations. These meetings discuss scientific problems of importance to the conservation and wise exploitation of various fish stocks and the working groups may suggest cooperative research programs or recommend conservative methods.

Intergovernmental Fisheries Commissions have been established for specific areas or for particular species of fish. Those commissions to which the United States adheres are listed in Table 8. One objective of each commission is to conserve its given resource so that predictable harvests may be made year after year—in short to maintain a renewable resource, not one to be exploited to extinction. The earliest commission, The Pacific Fur Seal Commission, was established in 1911 after much international dispute and the reduction of the seal herd from nearly 5 million to a population of 125,000 over a period of about

TABLE 8. *International Fisheries Commissions Adhered to by the United States*

Great Lakes Fishery Commission (1955)
Inter-American Tropical Tuna Commission (1949)
North Pacific Fur Seal Commission (1911)
International North Pacific Fisheries Commission (1952)
International Pacific Halibut Commission (1924)
International Pacific Salmon Fisheries Commission (1937)
International Commission for Northwest Atlantic Fisheries (1949)
International Whaling Commission (1948)
International Atlantic Tuna Commission (1966)

---

40 years. Scientific study and enforced conservation practices have rebuilt the population so that an annual yield of nearly 100,000 is available on a continuing basis.

Another example is the work of the International Pacific Halibut Commission which was founded in 1924 when the annual yield of the fisheries had dropped to a low value of 44 million pounds. Again, scientifically based conservation practices allowed replenishment of the stock so that in 1968 annual production was 70 million pounds.

Not all of the commissions are so effective. Whaling in the Antarctic in 1968 had reached its lowest ebb, even though the International Whaling Commission had warned for years that the harvest was exceeding the ability of the population to reproduce itself. The commissions have no power to enforce regulations, and nations may refuse to sign treaties establishing conservation measures, and continue to harvest the unowned resources of the high seas.

The importance of the international fisheries commissions lies in the fact that they represent a concerted effort to base conservation methods on the best scientific information available, and that the objective is to achieve the maximum productivity of the fisheries on a renewable basis. If, however, an increase of the fish stock is achieved, the harvest may be increased either because the fish are easier to catch or because other nations' vessels may join in the lucrative fishery. When this happens, the stock may decrease again so that the lower annual yield is again established.

The old concept of the freedom of the seas was fine so long as the ocean was considered nearly worthless, except for cheap transportation or national defense. Management of the oceans for the exploitation of the natural resources that it contains, or that could be produced, demands a clarification of ownership.

Conclusion

For the purpose of this study we have emphasized marine resources. This neglects many other uses, both old and new, which man has made of the oceans. They have played a dominant role in our foreign policy and in our relations with other governments. At times the ocean has served as a moat between nations, separating them from their enemies. The seas have always served as a broad highway connecting nations for the transportation of essential goods to customers around the world. The use of the surface and the near-surface of the oceans is a vital aspect of the posture of navies throughout the world today. The use made of the whole ocean, in depth as well as extent, will be a chief concern of maritime nations in the future.

In emphasizing resources we should point out that a great deal more is known about the existence of these resources than about the means whereby they can be made useful to mankind. If it appears that the treatment in respect to projecting the use of these resources is conservative this arises from the fact that the ocean, as generations of seafaring people can testify, is a hostile environment. It is not an environment where an investor can rightfully expect a fast payoff but rather an environment which merits the most sophisticated sort of market analysis and technical evaluation before investing in marine projects. Profits will be made but not necessarily quickly. An investor should be prepared to make major long-term investments. The problems are difficult and unexpectedly tricky. They may be legal or economic, as well as technical.

Predictions are difficult but we would predict the largest increase in tapping the wealth of the oceans will be in oil and gas, sand and gravel, desalinated water, aquaculture and fish protein concentrate (FPC). More moderate increases will occur in the use of phosphorite and manganese nodules, placer minerals, extracted chemicals, and in the natural harvest of food and fish.

In spite of all these uncertainties the resources exist. They are generally within the reach of modern technology and will, it seems wholly reasonable to predict, be exploited by man when it is economically profitable to do so. Therefore, it is of great importance and great urgency to solve the legal and diplomatic problems in an orderly manner and timely way, and thus permit a cooperative and peaceful use of the wealth of nations.

Louis Henkin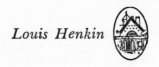

2

Changing Law for the Changing Seas

The law of the sea, one of the oldest and strongest members of the body of international law, has seen great change in our day. Additional needs calling for additional uses in additional parts of the sea, and advancing technology making new uses possible, have strained accepted norms and inspired new law. Coastal states have successfully asserted increased rights in wider areas. Nuclear powers have temporarily appropriated large sections of the high seas for testing. The need to avoid conflict and to conserve resources has led to new cooperative legal arrangements about fishing. The United Nations Charter, in outlawing war, has cast doubt upon all the traditional lore about the rights and obligations of neutrals and belligerents that made up so much of yesterday's law of the sea.

Now the sea's new promises—of untold resources soon within reach, of a new environment hospitable to human sojourn and activity—portend even more radical change in the law. The growing threat of destruction from the sea also inspires hopes of achieving law to control military uses there. Already many challenge the basic concept of traditional law—that political slogan subsuming legal norms, "the freedom of the seas;" we must, we are told, abandon freedom, and—as in other environments—leave laissez-faire behind and move toward regulation for the common welfare. Already schools are forming, differing as to how much regulation, what kind, how soon.

LOUIS HENKIN *is Hamilton Fish Professor of International Law and Diplomacy at Columbia University. He was for many years an officer of the Department of State, in the Bureau of United Nations Affairs and in the Bureau of European Affairs. He has written and lectured widely on U.S. foreign affairs. Professor Henkin edited the American Assembly volume* Arms Control.

In these pages I suggest the frontiers that are being challenged, the claims that are being made, the directions in which we are being pointed. I attempt a brief statement—inevitably skeletal and over-simple—of existing law governing the principal uses of the sea, set forth the legal issues that have arisen or loom ahead, and suggest what law and legal arrangements might develop. For the purposes of this volume, my emphasis is principally on the law governing extraction of the sea's resources, but I say something, too, about regulation of military uses and scientific research, and, glancingly, other uses as well.

The Law as It Is

To describe the law of the sea "as it is" is to describe a law some of which is uncertain, much of which is in flux. The general principles, however, have remained, the principal exceptions are agreed, the areas and directions of change are identifiable.

THE PRINCIPLE OF FREEDOM

For hundreds of years the basic principle of the law of the seas has been freedom. With it—or beneath it—has been the principle that the sea belonged to everyone, or to no one. In particular, unlike land, the sea could not be acquired by nations and made subject to national sovereignty.

Freedom of the seas has meant freedom to use the seas, and no uses have been barred. The principal use has been navigation—for fishing, trade, travel, war. In time, the seas began to lend themselves to tunneling, laying of cables, submarine travel, scientific research. Today, the seas are a principal area of military deployment and manoeuvre and harbor "permanently" sophisticated military weapons and equipment. The seas have recreational and scientific importance. They have long been a repository for waste, recently also for atomic waste. Unless modified, the principle of freedom would presumably apply also to future uses—to transportation, sojourn, or other human activity in the waters below or on the sea bed.

Freedom has extended also to the air above the seas and it, too, has been open to all for aviation and its various purposes. There has been no agreement, however, as to "who owns the seabed," as to whether the "commonage" of the seas applies as well to the seabed and its subsoil. Some have urged that the seas are not subject to national acquisition only because that would interfere with freedom, particularly for navigation, but there is no similar reason for denying national acquisition and sovereignty in the seabed and its subsoil.

Freedom of the seas, and the principle that they belong to all, or none, has meant also freedom for all nations to exploit sea resources, principally to fish and to keep one's catch. Those who insisted that the seas were common property might have had difficulty explaining why individual nations could appropriate the fish that belonged to all. But the theoretical questions bothered only theoreticians. Fishing was older than international law; no nation had any interest in insisting that fishing was generally prohibited; besides, the fish reproduced themselves and seemed plentiful and inexhaustible. Even when it proved that fish were not in fact always and everywhere plentiful and inexhaustible, the freedom to fish in the seas at large survived unimpaired. It seemed unlikely that a different rule would apply as man began to extract other resources, organic or inorganic, from the waters, or to the waters themselves, although questions might arise if new processes for extraction required major, "permanent" installations that unduly interfered with navigation or other established rights.

Again, there has been disagreement as to whether the resources on or beneath the seabed are similarly subject to appropriation by anyone. Until today, the resources of the seabed could be exploited only in coastal waters by coastal states and, we shall see, the law has confirmed their right to these resources to the exclusion of other nations. If, however, it is now (or will soon be) possible for any nation to extract a wealth of oil and manganese in parts of the sea far from any coast, may it lawfully do so, and, if so, on what terms, subject to what limitations? Or are these minerals the property of all, not to be extracted at all without the consent of "the community," and only on its terms?

The precedents have been few and special: a handful of cases where a nation—usually the coastal nation—claimed historic rights to fish for pearls or sedentary fish in coastal waters, or tunneled for minerals from shore. Theoretical arguments may be found for either side of the argument although until recently the question hardly interested even the theoreticians. Writers who consider that the seabed and its subsoil are subject to national acquisition and sovereignty tend to conclude that the resources on or beneath the bed are also subject to be taken by any nation. Those who take the view that the seabed and subsoil, like the sea and air above, are not subject to national sovereignty, are more likely to insist that the resources of the bed and subsoil belong to all and may not be seized by any nation for its exclusive benefit. Presumably, they would distinguish the right of any nation to catch and keep fish as a historical exception antedating modern law, based partly on the fact that fish reproduce themselves and on the view, however mistaken, that their supply was inexhaustible. The cases in which coastal nations claimed sedentary fishes and minerals also reflect historical exceptions in limited areas, antedating the principle of the freedom of the sea and the recognition of its common ownership.

LIMITATIONS ON FREEDOM

Like all law, the various laws of the seas may be seen as derogations from the principle of freedom. The freedom of the sea is, of course, subject to general law that applies at sea as elsewhere, for example rules protecting persons and property, or the law of the U.N. Charter outlawing war and other uses of force. There are limitations in special laws and agreements that have applied only, or especially, at sea—for example, those against piracy or slave-running, or wartime limitations on trade between neutrals and belligerents.

For our purposes, there is a limitation on freedom in the view that law excludes other nations from excavating where one nation has staked out a claim. There are different limitations in the other view—that no nation may seize the resources of the ocean bed. I stress also two special orders of limitation. The law has recognized special rights for coastal nations in coastal areas, limiting the freedom of other nations in those areas. (Other nations have acquired special rights, usually through long usage, to carry on particular activities in particular parts of the sea, *e.g.,* "historic" fishing rights.) There are inevitable limitations on freedom when different nations compete to use the same areas for the same or different purposes, and the law regulates this competition.

RIGHTS OF COASTAL STATES

It is universally accepted that the coastal state enjoys special rights in areas of the sea adjacent to its coasts; some coastal nations have claimed additional rights that are strongly disputed.

The territorial sea—Beyond its "internal waters"—rivers, gulfs, bays, harbors—the law gives every coastal nation a maritime belt, "the territorial sea." As the designation suggests, in this part of the sea the coastal nation exercises full sovereignty over the waters, the air space, the seabed; the coastal state, then, has exclusive rights to all its uses and all its resources, subject to "historic rights" to fish which other nations may have acquired, and to rights given to other nations by treaty. But international law recognizes a right of "innocent passage" through these waters, at least for non-military vessels, and fishing, mining and other activities by the coastal state must not interfere unduly with such passage.

The big issue about the territorial sea is how wide it is. Claims vary widely, from three nautical miles (a position shared by the United States) to 200 miles, claimed by some Latin American states. International conferences on the law of the sea, in 1958 and 1960 at Geneva, struggled with these differences but produced no agreement. The United States supported a compromise—a six mile territorial sea and an additional six miles of contiguous zone in which the coastal state would have exclusive fishing rights (subject to some historic rights for others); but when the compromise failed of adoption—by a narrow margin—the United States reverted to the three mile zone. The issue is unresolved, but the overwhelming majority of nations are agreed that the territorial sea is no wider than 12 miles. (In the *Pueblo* incident, in January 1968, North Korea claimed that the American vessel was within its 12-mile territorial sea. While the United States does not recognize the 12-mile claim, it presumably had no intention to challenge it in this case. The issue was complicated by the fact that the Korean Armistice Agreement requires each side to respect the "waters contiguous" to the land under control of the other side, a phrase that may suggest the "contiguous zone" of international law now commonly accepted as 12 miles.)

Fishing zones—A principal motive for claims to a wide territorial sea has been the desire of coastal nations to exclude alien fishermen, in order to protect domestic fishing interests, sometimes also to permit effective conservation. (Some of the Latin American nations that have made extravagant claims to a territorial sea of 200 miles have sought to enforce only exclusive fishing rights in that area.) Other nations have explicitly begun to claim special fishing zones: The United States, for example, while reverting to a three-mile territorial sea, has recently claimed a 12-mile exclusive fishing zone.

Contiguous zones—International law has come to recognize special rights for the coastal state in a "contiguous zone" beyond the territorial sea, up to 12 miles from the coast. In this zone the coastal state may exercise controls necessary to prevent or punish infringement of its customs, fiscal, immigration or sanitary regulations.

Other zones have been asserted but have not been widely accepted. Some states have claimed the right to establish "security zones." During the Second World War the nations of the Western Hemisphere purported to establish for "continental self-protection" a "neutrality zone" (extending several hundred miles from shore in some places) from which they sought to bar "any hostile act by any non-American belligerent nation." The United States (and Canada) have also established air defense identification zones extending several hundred miles out to sea, requiring pilots of foreign aircraft headed for the United States (or Canada) to identify themselves and to comply with regulations.

Coastal states have also asserted auxiliary rights beyond the zones described. International law has recognized the right of "hot pursuit," permitting the coastal nation to pursue violators of its laws, from its contiguous waters out to sea. Recently coastal states have asserted the right to act against "pirate" vessels or stations at sea that broadcast into their territory without license or consent.

The continental shelf—A major contemporary extension of the rights of the coastal state is the law of the continental shelf. Based largely on the Truman Proclamation of 1945, the law has been codified in one of the Geneva conventions of 1958, the Convention on the Continental Shelf. Although only a minority of the world's states have adhered to that Convention, no one has seriously challenged its basic doctrine and it is commonly accepted as universal law.

The 1958 Convention gives the coastal nation sovereign rights on its continental shelf (as defined) for the purposes of exploring the shelf and exploiting its resources (including the sedentary fishes on the seabed). Those who take the view that the bed of the sea, unlike the seas above, is subject to national acquisition, may see the new law of the shelf as an exception: because of the special interests of the coastal state, other nations are denied the right to occupy this seabed, while coastal nations have sovereign rights to the bed for limited purposes without the need for occupation or other act of acquisition. Those who insist that the seabed generally is not subject to national sovereignty also see the law of the shelf as an exception, by general consensus, giving coastal nations limited sovereignty for a single purpose.

For mining purposes, then, the continental shelf is the equivalent of territorial sea, and the width of the territorial sea is immaterial since wherever it ends the continental shelf begins. For other purposes, however, the waters above the shelf remain "high seas" free to all nations for other uses.

THE LAW OF "CONFLICTING USES"

Freedom of the seas for all has meant of course that no state was free to exclude others. From the beginning, too, freedom had to give way to "conflicting uses"—if only between two vessels seeking to ply the same waters, or nations competing to fish in the same area. As uses of the sea grew, the possibilities of conflict grew. Even navigation and fishing had to accommodate each other. Later, ships had to watch out for cables, and recently for oil derricks, sea mounts, scientific buoys; submarines might run afoul of diving gear, installations on the seabed or military detection equipment. Nuclear tests prevented all other uses in large areas of seas for short periods. Other military uses, operations and pollutions might bar other uses for long times.

Early, as freedom led to conflict, conflict led to some regulation. Friendly nations began to leave each other alone, to develop navigation lanes, rules of navigation, laws about collisions and other mishaps at sea. General recognition of the special rights of coastal states helped to reduce conflict. As regards fishing, in particular, in some areas and for some species, there grew a network of international agreements designed to accommodate the claims of coastal states and of others, of states with historical rights and of newcomers, and to make some provision for conservation. Infrequently, nations also entered agreements determining their respective rights in other resources, for example, the 1942 agreement between Great Britain and Venezuela with respect to mineral resources in the Gulf of Paria.

Some law grew also to regulate conflicts between different uses. The law developed principles of priority and some general standards of conduct. Traditionally, navigation has been a preferred use, and interferences with navigation (in time of peace) have been strongly resisted. (That nuclear tests at sea interfered with navigation, albeit temporarily, was a principal argument of those who considered them illegal.) "Reasonableness" has frequently been invoked as the standard of behavior: There may be "reasonable" interferences with some uses to promote others; when uses conflict there must be a "reasonable" balancing of interests to determine which use is to be preferred.

Conflicting uses are also the subject of agreement. In the nineteenth century agreements provided for the protection of oceanic cables. The 1958 Geneva conventions on the law of the sea, while codifying the principle of freedom, also included basic provisions to regulate conflicting uses. The Convention on the Continental Shelf, for example, provides that, subject to its right to take "reasonable measures" to explore the shelf and exploit its mineral resources, the coastal state may not interfere with laying cables or pipelines. Mining "must not result in any unjustifiable interference with navigation, fishing or the conservation of the living resources of the sea." Installations and safety zones around them must not interfere with "recognized sea lanes essential to international navigation." Mining must not "result in any interference with fundamental oceanographic or other scientific research carried out with the intention of open publication." And research on and concerning the continental shelf requires the consent of the coastal state but such consent shall be normally granted.

To sum up, with emphasis on our principal concerns: the coastal state enjoys exclusive jurisdiction for all purposes in a territorial sea of disputed width, probably no greater than 12 miles. The coastal state also has sovereignty for purposes of exploiting mineral resources on the continental shelf, as defined. Some states also claim a fishing zone, in many instances out to 12 miles from shore.

Apart from the rights of the coastal state, the law permits free use of the high seas for all purposes, including military deployments, though not, of course, for acts in violation of any treaty, for example, the Nuclear Test Ban or the U.N. Charter. Conflicting uses must be reasonably accommodated, and navigation and scientific research in particular are not to be unduly hindered, even on the continental shelf.

As regards the sea's resources, fish are up for catching, subject to the rights of the coastal state in coastal zones, to historic rights of other nations and to special treaty arrangements. Other resources in the waters of the sea are probably subject to a similar regime. The minerals on and below the seabed of the territorial sea and on the continental shelf belong exclusively to the coastal state. As regards the deep ocean bed, there is no agreement whether it is subject to national acquisition and sovereignty, or whether, without such acquisition, its resources may be extracted and appropriated by any nation at will.

Issues and Problems

The law as it is raises issues and presents problems. Some are due to the law's uncertainties, others to old or new inadequacies in the law. Uncertainties are not necessarily undesirable, to those in a position to take advantage of them. Whether the law is adequate or not will also depend on differing interests and perspectives.

As regards military uses, the law of the sea is basically one of laissez-faire. There are no major uncertainties that relate to the sea as such (as distinguished from the law of military uses generally). There is, of course, the uncertainty as to the status of all the laws of war that applied at sea before the U.N. Charter, but hopefully that question will remain largely academic. There is still debate as to the lawfulness of nuclear tests at sea, but most nations have forsworn such tests, and any nation that decides to test at sea will no doubt invoke the precedent of earlier tests and the legal justifications then offered. It is not clear what special security measures a coastal state may take either in its contiguous zone, or on the continental shelf, or beyond. There is uncertainty as to whether the right of innocent passage in the territorial sea applies to military vessels. And the uncertainty as to the width of the territorial sea has important military consequences since a wider territorial sea effectively bars military uses in more of the sea, and may completely bar important "international" straits to military vessels and other military deployments.

Clarification of some of these issues, at least, would be desirable. Most suggestions for new law in relation to military uses, however, would seek not to clarify ambiguities but to regulate that which is now permitted, perhaps also to permit some things now forbidden. Mostly, they are arms control or disarmament proposals. I consider them below.

Scientific research, too, suffers few major legal uncertainties, though the law's application may be uncertain: for example, it is often difficult to know where research ends and exploration for resources begins. On the high seas research is free but suffers some of the inadequacies of laissez-faire. It suffers as well from undue concern for national security by both researching nations and states near whose shores they may operate. There are no arrangements for general cooperation, for protecting buoys and scientific equipment. Lack of uniformity in research practices and in markings creates dangers for both research and for navigation.

The tendency of coastal states to increase their jurisdiction has had particularly unfortunate consequences for scientific research. Claiming more extensive internal waters and territorial sea, nations have barred them to research by foreign nationals. On the continental shelf, although the Convention provides that mining must not interfere with scientific research, in fact it does. The coastal state is not normally to withhold consent to carry on research "on" and "concerning" the continental shelf, but consent has not always been forthcoming from all nations.

Fishing, too, suffers less from legal uncertainties than from inadequate regulation and cooperation. The principal uncertainties in the relevant law lie in the disputed width of the territorial sea and in the validity and extent of special fishing zones declared by many coastal nations. There are also disputed claims of historic rights and issues of interpretation and application of various agreements.

Few would argue that fishing does not need new legal controls and cooperative institutions. Fishing techniques are inefficient and research is inadequate. There is duplication of capitalization and of effort. There is little thought to conservation and depletion of the oceans is not a wild fear. In some areas there is congestion leading to danger of collision and conflict. Inefficiency as well as conflict have also been promoted by the claims of coastal nations to exclusive rights in increasing areas of coastal waters. The network of treaty arrangements has grown but their coverage is limited and they are not coordinated.

For the extraction of other materials, organic or inorganic, from the waters of the seas the relevant law is freedom, subject to conflicting uses. As yet there is little cry for regulation of competition or of conflict with other uses. Issues may arise especially if complex processes and extensive installations begin to interfere with navigation or fishing or to pollute the seas.

Perhaps because there is actual commercial and political interest inducing a spate of writing and debate, the law governing mineral resources on the seabed and subsoil seems most beset by uncertainty and inadequacies, its law in greatest need of clarification and modification.

There is little dissatisfaction with the law that gives the coastal state exclusive rights to exploit the resources of the bed of its territorial sea or of its continental shelf. Some question that provision which applies the doctrine of the shelf to give the coastal state exclusive rights in sedentary fishes; among other objections, this requires the difficult drawing of unreasonable lines between fishes and fishes.

Except in regard to scientific research, the 1958 Convention of the shelf also provides more-or-less adequately for avoiding conflict with other uses. Inevitably, however, extensive operations involving permanent installations have in fact interfered with navigation and other uses. Despite regulations and precautions there have been collisions between vessels and mining installations or equipment. Explosives used in exploration for minerals have interfered with fishing and killed fish. With regulation and control by the coastal state, fishing and military activities on the continental shelf of another nation are becoming increasingly difficult. Many consider it inevitable that interference will increase, greater regulation by the coastal state will be necessary, and sovereignty in the coastal state for purposes of mining will expand and become sovereignty for other or all purposes. The United States, for example, has extended the application of its laws to the continental shelf. Although the 1958 Convention provides that the waters above the shelf are high seas, there is some tendency to treat the waters above the shelf as "contiguous zone" and there have been suggestions that the law be modified to that effect so as to legitimate what states will inevitably do.

The Definition of the Shelf

The big issue about the continental shelf is its legal definition. The 1958 Convention defines the shelf as:

> . . . the seabed and subsoil of the submarine areas adjacent to the coast but outside the area of the territorial sea, to a depth of 200 meters or, beyond that limit, to where the depth of the superjacent waters admits of the exploitation of the natural resources of the said area. . . .

The legal definition of the shelf, I stress, is not the geological definition. It includes areas that are not continental shelf at all in a geological sense—like the bed of the Persian Gulf, whose waters are less than 200 feet deep; it also includes areas beyond the geological shelf when it ends in waters less than 200 meters deep. Excluded from the basic legal definition are those parts of the geological shelf extending into waters more than 200 meters deep. Wholly unrelated to geology, of course, is the second part of the definition, the "exploitability clause:" the legal continental shelf extends beyond the 200 meter isobath in waters where the natural resources can in fact be exploited.

When this definition was adopted, the 200 meter isobath was considered approximately the limit at which mining was technically possible; exploitation in substantially deeper waters, it was assumed, would not be possible before many years. The exploitability clause was added principally at the behest of countries that had no geological shelf, whose coasts dropped sheerly into deep waters: since the 200 meter definition would give them nothing, the exploitability clause was added to give them "equal treatment" in principle. The "exploitability clause" was supported, secondly, by the view that if it became possible for the coastal state to exploit somewhat beyond the 200 meter isobath its right to do so should be clear without waiting for renegotiation of the Convention. Technology, however, has again outdistanced legal expectations and now, we are told, minerals can be exploited virtually anywhere at sea, regardless of depth of waters. If so, under the Convention, where do the exclusive mineral rights of the coastal state end?

There have been various suggestions. Some have urged that the Convention be interpreted literally: a coastal nation's legal shelf, and its right to exploit resources, go on indefinitely—until, say in mid-ocean, it meets the shelf of another nation. (The Convention already provides for the division of a shelf shared by adjoining states. The provision will probably be interpreted in a decision by the International Court of Justice about the appropriate division of the resources of the North Sea.) For purpose of mineral resources, then, the oceans would be "international lakes," their seabed divided up among the nations that border it. Others have suggested that the exploitability clause should stop at the geological shelf: a nation may claim resources beyond the 200 meter depth only so long as the area is still on the geological shelf. Yet another suggestion would determine exploitability by the technology of some particular date, say 1958 when the Convention was adopted, or 1964 when it came into effect. A fourth suggestion would end the shelf at the 200 meter isobath for nations that have a geological shelf, leaving the exploitability clause for nations that have no real shelf, for whose benefit, principally, the clause was added.

None of these suggestions has intrinsic merit, in terms of what the authors of the Convention intended, and some are basically inconsistent with the philosophy and purposes of the Convention. In particular, the suggestion that all the seabed be divided among the coastal nations would be a "grab," unacceptable even to many coastal nations that might profit from it. The United States would oppose it because sovereignty in coastal states for mining purposes tends to extend to other uses and would jeopardize the whole principle of free seas. Other nations might object for this and other reasons. Since the Convention gives a "continental shelf" also to every island, the division of the seabed would not be a simple matter and would give windfalls to nations that have far-flung, happily-located, island possessions. While no one has yet considered in detail what this proposal would give to which countries, it appears, for example, that the Soviet Union would gain little from it, and would have little reason to support it.

If the limits of the continental shelf became a practical issue, one would have to work out some re-definition by re-interpretation. Some guidelines may be suggested: the Convention was defining a limited area and was to apply only to "submarine areas adjacent to the coast;" the doctrine of the shelf originated in and retains some relation to the geological shelf; the doctrine reflected a recognition that politically and technologically mining in the coastal area could be done only by the coastal state or with its cooperation, and that the coastal state had a legitimate objection to major, permanent foreign installations close to its shores. At some point, surely—not far from shore—an area ceases to be adjacent, indeed to have any relation whatever to any coast, and coastal states have no greater rights or interests than any other. Even with such guidelines, however, it would be difficult to argue the illegality of leases in any "adjacent" waters, which might include waters of any depth and even, say, 100 miles from shore.

Nations have already begun to exploit beyond the 200 meter isobath. The United States, for example, has been issuing leases beyond that depth; it has not refused any lease on the ground that the area to be explored is in waters that are too deep or too far from shore, and therefore beyond the shelf and outside the jurisdiction of the United States. In view of the flexible definition of the shelf it would be difficult to call any such exploitations illegal. One may expect slow—and not so slow—appropriation of additional areas of the seabed where the geological shelf extends into deeper waters, and even on the continental slope, unless nations exercise self-restraint or join to revise the Convention to put an outer limit to the shelf.

The open-ended definition is an asset in the hands of every coastal nation (and island government), permitting it to claim an ever-increasing shelf as technology makes exploration possible in deeper waters farther from shore. But even coastal nations have interests other than minerals. The United States, for example, has to decide whether exclusive rights in additional minerals in its coastal waters is worth: the price of having other coastal nations acquire similar exclusive rights; the dangers which broad continental shelves under the jurisdiction of other nations would create for American interests in military uses of those areas, in scientific research or fishing there; the consequences for the traditional American policy of limited exclusive national rights and maximum freedom at sea; and the longer, larger political and economic consequences of letting the coastal states "grab" more and more of the sea's resources. An outer limit might be necessary to safeguard competing national interests; eventually, too, the definition of the shelf should be clarified to avoid confusion and conflict.

There are issues, then, as to whether nations should seek formal redefinition, and if so, when. (Under the Convention any party can seek revision five years after the agreement came into effect, *i.e.*, beginning in June 1969.) There are issues as to what new definition of the shelf should emerge. Whether and when a state might desire redefinition would depend on how content it is with present ambiguity, as compared with what any new definition likely to be achieved would offer. Pending any formal redefinition nations have to decide what definition they will live by, and what definitions (or practices reflecting definitions) by others they will acquiesce in or challenge.

EXPLOITING THE RESOURCES OF THE DEEP SEA

As to the law governing the extraction of minerals from the deep seabed, the only certainty is that the law is uncertain. It is not clear whether any nation can acquire, and claim sovereignty in, the seabed, and, if so, by what measures. It is not clear whether, without any claims of sovereignty, any state (or private entrepreneur) can lawfully proceed to dig and keep what it extracts. And what protections would the miner have against poaching or interference?

Here the uncertainty results in opposing tendencies. On the one hand in some quarters it tends to discourage exploration of the sea's resources. It is commonly accepted that successful, economic mining requires that the entrepreneur have exclusive rights to explore a sizable area of seabed and exploit any "strike" for a long term of years. Sound conservative companies—and their bankers—will be reluctant to invest the huge expenditures of effort and capital involved, without substantial assurance that they will enjoy the fruits undisturbed and unchallenged. Especially since there are fertile fields still untapped on the continental shelf or what might pass as shelf under the open-ended definition (since even under a conservative definition it has been estimated that only some 15 per cent of the shelf has been explored), conservative enterprise might concentrate its efforts there and hesitate to venture into deep ocean.

On the other hand, an uncertain law will not deter the venturesome. Governments, less concerned for their investments, may enter the race, if only for political reasons, for military reasons, for scientific and technological experience. Venturesome private entrepreneurs, too, might risk it, assuming that, if issues developed, their governments will feel compelled to give them legal and diplomatic support. Moreover, they might consider the danger of challenge of competition and conflict exaggerated: at least for a while, the few nations—or companies— that have the capital and the "know-how" would probably leave each other alone in the rich and spacious seas.

It is open to debate, then, whether the uncertain law will encourage or discourage exploitation of the sea's resources, or encourage the "right" or "wrong" kind of exploitation. There are differences, too, as to how the present law affects other national interests of different countries. To some extent, surely the law's uncertainty is an asset for wealthy, technologically-advanced, venturesome countries. The United States could begin to claim parts of the deep seabed; or, without such claims, it could encourage its nationals to proceed to dig, assuring them diplomatic and legal protection. Nations without a technology of their own could "sell" their protection to venturesome entrepreneurs, as they do their "flag" as a convenience to vessels.

But, again, nations have interests other than minerals, and policy makers would have to consider whether a law of "free-for-all" is in the over-all national interest. A law that permits national acquisition of the seabed might lead to claims of sovereignty for other purposes as well, and interfere with military, scientific and other uses. Such a law —or even one that only permits digging at will—might lead to controversy and conflict of the kind that troubled the age of discovery. And it would foreclose a new and passing opportunity to make a bold departure and dedicate a new universe to international cooperation and welfare. In July 1966, President Johnson said:

> Under no circumstances, we believe, must we ever allow the prospects of rich harvest and mineral wealth to create a new form of colonial competition among the maritime nations. We must be careful to avoid a race to grab and to hold the lands under the high seas. We must ensure that the deep seas and the ocean bottoms are, and remain, the legacy of all human beings.

This statement is not without its ambiguities, but its spirit is enlightened, even noble. Other, more recent pronouncements have been more reserved. Resolutions have been introduced in Congress, most of which have a very different flavor and are, at best, cautious. Other countries, too, are beginning to identify their interests and are reaching different views as to what law should govern mining beyond the continental shelf.

There are differences within and between nations as to the adequacy of the present uncertain law. One issue often raised is that of timing: some have urged that it is premature to make new law before some of the sea's promises are realized, before there is experience instead of speculation as to the problems to which law must address itself. Such views may reflect estimates that deep-sea mining is yet some years away, but to some extent, at least, they imply, too, that in its early phases such mining can be satisfactorily developed under existing uncertain law. Others insist that there be some new law from the beginning of the age of deep-sea mining, lest the daring of some nations and the indifference of most others shape the future law in undesirable ways. Such concerns were no doubt implied in initiatives like that of the Government of Malta when it put this subject on the agenda of the U.N. General Assembly in 1967.

(A nation's views as to the urgency of developing law for the deep ocean will be affected also by its policy on the width of the continental shelf. A nation that claims a wide shelf will to that extent care less about the law that applies beyond and will feel less urgency about clarifying that law. A decision to narrow the shelf gives the law of the deep sea greater and earlier relevance.)

Proposals for New Law

Proposals for new law have been cropping up with increasing frequency, differing widely in basic philosophy, in scope, and in the care and detail with which they have been prepared.

There is some talk of a new comprehensive law of the sea, and outer space is sometimes invoked as a model for a law of "hydrospace." In fact, the present law of outer space is hardly a comprehensive law: it consists principally of a few general principles and one arms control provision. It does not anticipate law for any of the many imaginative uses which are promised for a future day. In any event, in my view, outer space is not a precedent in point and does not afford an apt analogy for a law of the deep sea. Outer space is a new environment, separate and isolable, without vested national interests or other national commitments. The nations presently interested in space are few and its "uses" are hypothetical and uncertain. By contrast, the sea has a long history of various uses by a hundred nations, and uses and nations increase steadily. A new law of the sea would challenge old accepted ways and modify old accepted laws.

Whatever the precedents or analogies, a comprehensive new law for the sea is not now feasible, and perhaps not desirable. The last effort, in 1958, produced several discrete conventions, mostly codifying existing law. It is surely premature to anticipate the new uses promised and to establish principles for their regulation. On the other hand, it may be time to deal anew with segments of the law of the sea where the need for new law is clear and the problems visible. Nations may be reluctant to jeopardize the general principle of freedom or to tamper with particular uses—*e.g.*, military uses—but may readily see the desirability of some new principle or new regulation as regards, say, mining of the sea's resources. At the same time, it is important to consider the consequences that law for some uses may have on others.

One law with "comprehensive" consequences that has been suggested would give to the U.N. "title" to or "sovereignty" over the ocean bed beyond the continental shelf. That, presumably, would give the U.N. authority to determine all uses of the seabed. I deal with this suggestion below in the context of particular uses.

MILITARY USES

The law governing military uses at sea can be importantly affected by changes in law of general applicability, for example by agreements eliminating or controlling the use of some weapon. In a different way new agreement on a wider territorial sea may effectively bar military vessels and equipment from additional areas of sea, and even a wider continental shelf will tend to discourage military uses there. In deep sea, too, a general law aimed at other uses can affect military uses as well, as in the proposals to give the U.N. sovereignty or other rights in the seabed, discussed below.

Suggestions for new law about the military uses in particular take different forms and have different goals. Some have written about the need to protect, even promote, military uses, at least "defensive" ones: for example, law could expressly permit, and protect against violation by others, national "hardened" submarine rocket installations, fixed submarine maintenance facilities, research and communications stations, storage depots, repair works, or other submarine "strategic areas." Similarly, some foresee the need for regulating "traffic" in submarine military vehicles as they increase in quantity and mobility.

Usually, suggestions for regulating military uses propose various forms of disarmament or arms control in the sea. (Suggestions for protecting submarine military installations would also have some arms control qualities since they would require identification and disclosure of the installations.) Arms control proposals take different forms. One kind is typified by a proposal to establish a sea-wide network of buoys and equipment for detecting and tracking submarines. The network might be operated by some international authority. Most proposals would demilitarize or exclude particular weapons from all or parts of the sea. Recently attention has focused in particular on the seabed: some have proposed that it be wholly demilitarized, while others would at least exclude weapons of mass destruction. Supporters of such proposals usually invoke the precedent of outer space, where by U.N. resolution and subsequent treaty, nations agreed not to place weapons of mass destruction in orbit around the earth, on celestial bodies, or anywhere in space. (Antarctica, too, has been reserved by treaty for peaceful purposes only and nuclear explosions have been barred there for any purposes. The Spitsbergen Treaty of 1920 also barred militarization of that area.) But, again, in these and other cases, nations forewent what they did not yet have, had never relied on, perhaps could not appreciate. In the sea, military vessels and weapons are an integral and dominant element of national defense, for many nations; submarine-based missiles, indeed, are key weapons in global strategy, on which deterrence, security and perhaps world peace depend. Precedents and analogies apart, the United States surely will not give up its Navy and its submarine-based missiles, except—theoretically—in some final stage of general and complete disarmament.

On the other hand, it is not out of the question to consider the demilitarization of some parts of the sea, the elimination or control of some weapons or some uses. (Nuclear-testing underwater and in the atmosphere—including the air space above the seas—is forbidden by the Nuclear Test Ban of 1963.) While demilitarizing the seabed without demilitarizing the sea might contribute little to peace and military stability, it might forestall fixed military complexes and atomic "caches" that would be more difficult to eliminate or control later; it might also serve as another small step to slow down the arms race. Whether such proposals are feasible and acceptable is not clear. The ambiguous content of the term "demilitarization" would be especially discouraging. There is no indication that nations have already stationed weapons of mass destruction on the seabed or that the right to do so looms large in future plans for national deterrence systems. On the other hand, the United States, and probably the Soviet Union, apparently have considerable, sophisticated "military equipment" on the seabed, *e.g.*, submarine detection devices. It is unlikely that the United States would agree to sacrifice them, and it is not clear that any agreement to that end could be effectively monitored. Proposals that would bar the seabed to weapons of mass destruction might also entail inspection problems, and a system to verify a ban on such weapons might interfere with submarine detection systems and perhaps other uses of the seabed. For these and other reasons some believe that, unlike outer space, proposals for controlling arms in the sea or on the seabed cannot be simple, and would hold more promise in a context of negotiation about disarmament rather than about the law of the sea.

It seems unlikely, then, that the United States would agree to a U.N. resolution "demilitarizing" the seabed; it might also be reluctant to agree to exclude weapons of mass destruction. Surely, it is not likely to accept a resolution granting to the U.N. complete sovereignty over the seabed, since such unqualified sovereignty would presumably subject all military uses of the seabed to the control of majority votes in the General Assembly.

SCIENTIFIC RESEARCH

The principal problem has been restriction of research by the coastal state in the territorial sea and on the continental shelf. It has been suggested that there be established a principle of "innocent research," analogous to "innocent passage," even in the territorial sea. (The interests of the coastal state might be safeguarded by a requirement that its nationals be permitted to participate in all research.) In regard to the continental shelf there are several ambiguities in the requirement that the consent of the coastal state be obtained "in respect of any research concerning the continental shelf and undertaken there." And while the Convention provides that such consent shall not "normally" be withheld, a firmer undertaking may be necessary to assure that research will in fact be permitted. In all parts of the sea, new law might also provide for cooperation in research, for procedures and markings that will reduce danger and conflict with navigation and other uses.

FISHING

There is a growing movement to adopt a 12-mile coastal fishing zone, subject, perhaps, to historic rights. This would eliminate an area of conflict and reduce temptations to claim a 12-mile territorial sea. Overall, there have been calls for new approaches that would promote efficiency and conservation, divide or allocate ocean fishing resources, avoid conflict, reduce interference with other uses of the sea. Among alternatives that have been discussed are:

1. Comprehensive internationalization that would allow an international authority to run the fisheries of the world.
2. Establishment of an international agency with authority to develop and enforce conservation regulation.
3. The negotiation of a comprehensive treaty establishing the fishing rights of different nations and creating an international agency to enforce the treaty. (The treaty might even require a fishing license from the agency.)
4. A right of "innocent fishing" which would allow fishing (and fishing research) by all nations even in coastal waters.

In a brief chapter, one can say only that these suggestions represent more or less radical solutions for the grave problems that beset the fishing industry. There is little basis for confidence, or even hope, that any of these solutions is likely to be attempted in the near future. Comprehensive internationalization to replace national fishing seems out of the question. And coastal nations are not likely to agree to "innocent fishing." The problem, then, will remain that of achieving some accommodation between competition and conservation, between coastal nations and others, between nations with some historic claims in an area and newcomers. It may be difficult to achieve agreement on a universal treaty with a universal formula. But, whether universally or regionally, new agreements are necessary, as are new institutions with additional functions. An international body to develop and enforce a conservation program would seem a basic need. A licensing body is a more ambitious undertaking in a context where freedom and laissez-faire have been the rule. Nations might look with greater favor on this suggestion if they accepted the principle of licensing in other contexts where the history and the problems are different, as in regard to mineral resources, discussed below.

MINERAL RESOURCES

The principal focus of proposals for new law has been on mineral resources. That law would be affected, of course, by changes of general applicability; for example, agreement on the width of the territorial sea would fix the area in which the coastal state has sovereignty, including sovereign rights to minerals. In fact, clarification of that law would not be especially significant for mineral resources since where the territorial sea ends the continental shelf begins, and every coastal nation has some continental shelf under present definitions. Some revisions in the definition of the shelf, of course, may make the width of the territorial sea a significant issue for mineral resources as well.

The law of the continental shelf cries for some revision. Although some of the reasons for that law have been overtaken by technology, few would suggest that the whole doctrine of the shelf be abandoned: law has been established, interests have vested, expectations have grown, and nations generally are content to let the coastal state keep the resources of the shelf. There are, however, proposals that would tighten the provisions to reduce conflict among uses; remove sedentary fishes from the doctrine; reexamine the principle that every island has a full "continental shelf."

Redefinition of the shelf—The principal preoccupation has been with the definition. All recognize its ambiguity but there is little agreement as to what to do about it. Some are content to do nothing, recognizing that as a result coastal states might extend their claims to mineral resources, even onto the continental slope, perhaps beyond it. Others have urged redefinition, dividing as to whether the new definition shall be broad or narrow. The former might propose a new depth limit—300, 500, 1000 or more meters—or a fixed distance from shore—25, 50, or 100 miles—or a definition combining depth and distance, for example, out to the 500 meter isobath and no farther than 100 miles from shore. (Some proposals would also give to every coastal state a *minimum* width of shelf so that states whose coasts drop into very deep water would also have a legal continental shelf.)

Proponents of a wide shelf emphasize that only the offer of a wide definition would persuade coastal nations to give up their present "open-ended" rights. A wide shelf would meet the legitimate concern of nations not to have near their shores permanent, extensive, foreign installations that might even mask activities dangerous to the coastal state's security. It would also encourage coastal states to be more enlightened about the character of the legal regime that would apply beyond the continental shelf. Even a broad definition would appropriate only a small portion of the total seabed. For example, the seabed out to the 200 meter isobath constitutes only 7.5 per cent of the total seabed; to the 2000 meter isobath, it would be 16.3 per cent; to 3000 meters, 24.8 per cent. See Menard & Smith, "Hypsometry of Ocean Basin Provinces," 71 *J. of Physical Research* 4305, 4314 (1966).

Others suggest a narrow shelf, perhaps the present definition without the exploitability clause: the shelf would end at the 200 meter isobath. If it is desirable to give something to coastal states with sheer coast lines, every coastal state could be given a minimum shelf, say out to 25 miles from its coasts. Proponents of the narrow shelf stress that a wide shelf is undesirable in principle since it interferes with some uses and threatens others. The wide shelf would be particularly serious if the definition continued to give every island a continental shelf. The result would be complex problems of dividing the seabed among overlapping claims, and windfalls for some nations with island possessions. Some of the original reasons for the shelf, moreover, no longer apply. The doctrine of the shelf was an exception to the "commonage" of the seas (outside the territorial sea), designed to encourage exploitation. But exploitation no longer depends on the coastal state, and it is now possible, and new law will soon make it permissible, to encourage exploitation in which all states participate or share equally. The only legitimate concern of coastal nations—to exclude foreign installations from their coastal waters—would usually be met even by a narrow shelf. It will surely be satisfied if the definition gives every coastal nation a minimum shelf x miles wide. I have suggested a variation: a narrow continental shelf (say, to the 200 meter isobath) plus a buffer zone out to *x* miles from shore which would be "deep ocean" and subject to whatever regime applies there, but in which mining could take place only by or with the consent of the coastal state.

Deep ocean-bed resources—There is even less agreement as to the urgency and the desirability of clarifying the law governing the exploitation of deep sea resources, not unrelated to sharp division as to what that law should be. The deepest differences reflect different guiding principles. Some insist that the paramount desideratum is that the resources be exploited as soon and as efficiently as possible, making them available for the needs of developing as well as developed societies. As in the case of the continental shelf, that requires law that encourages the states and the private entrepreneurs with technology and capital, by giving them a free hand, assuring them of the security of their investments, and promising them economic and other rewards. This can be achieved largely by accepting a few simple principles— that nations can acquire portions of the seabed; or, that, without such sovereignty, they can exploit the resources of the seabed as they can those of the sea, their operations being protected by their "flag" by analogy to vessels, the produce theirs to keep by analogy to fish. In time, as operations increase and there is risk of conflict, it will be desirable for nations to develop a code of competition. Some day it may be necessary to do more, to integrate mining into a comprehensive law of the sea including perhaps international regulatory institutions.

Another school considers that the paramount principle should be that the sea and its resources are a common heritage belonging to all mankind. The law of the continental shelf was an exception, inevitable when it developed and now probably irreversible. But the shelf should be limited and beyond the world's shelves no single nation has any special claims and no right to acquire any. Surely the community should not tolerate a race between nations to grab the resources for their own. Rather, it should assert "preventive law" to forestall such race and grab, assert its rights, proceed to arrange for exploration and exploitation on behalf of the community, make the products available, and apply the revenue to communal purposes. The new law needed to this end may take a few years to develop but there is no urgency to proceed, and, in any event, the delay is a necessary small price.

Behind these two general views and their variations lie differences of principle; there are also differences of assumption, appreciation, prognostication—about the quantities and location of resources, society's needs and capacities to absorb them, and other technological, economic and political factors present or anticipated. Whatever their origins the differences point to different views as to the authority of "the community" and how it shall be exercised, possible functions for international institutions, and different types of legal regime, generally characterized as "national" or "international."

I focus on the principal issues:

1. Does the U.N. have, or should it be given authority, to determine the disposition of the mineral resources of the deep seabed?
2. Shall the deep seabed be open to mining by states or only by some international authority?
3. If there is to be no international monopoly, may a state (itself, or by authorization to private companies) proceed to explore and extract resources at will, or shall it require some prior authorization from an international body?
4. What other authority and function might be entrusted to international institutions?
5. Should states (or companies) that mine the deep seas be required to pay a royalty, tax, or other fee and, if so, to whom for what purpose?
6. Should exploitation be subject to free competition, to competitive bidding, or to some other principle of preference or allocation among nations? Should there be a limit on the size of any "claim" which a nation is exploring, or on the number of claims any state may operate at any one time?

THE AUTHORITY OF THE UNITED NATIONS—In the first instance the differences and the issues are focused in the United Nations. Already there have been proposals, within and without the United Nations, that the General Assembly should adopt governing principles and proceed to implement them. The authority of the General Assembly to do so and the legal effect of what it does is not wholly agreed. In other fields, the Assembly has purported to declare existing principles of international law and to propose new ones. When these principles are not controversial, the Assembly's action has great weight, perhaps even legislative effect; even if there is some dissent, a declaration might be considered some kind of undertaking at least by the states that vote for it. In regard to the resources of the sea, there is stronger support for the authority of the Assembly if it is assumed that under existing law the resources of the sea belong to "the community." In that event the General Assembly might represent a close approximation of the common authority; in any event, since without authorization from the community no one can extract the minerals, there is likely to be less opposition to "authorizating legislation" by the Assembly.

Much will depend, of course, on what it is the General Assembly declares. A suggestion that it declare that the seabed and subsoil belongs to the United Nations might be effective politically and even legally, if all nations vote for it; it is almost certain, however, that it would meet strong opposition. The United States, surely, would not support a resolution giving title or sovereignty to the United Nations and thereby, presumably vesting in the Assembly authority, by two-thirds vote, to bar the seabed, say, to military uses.

Prospects might be somewhat more promising for a resolution that, taking a page out of the Convention on the Continental Shelf, would give the United Nations "sovereign rights for the purpose of exploring the deep seabed and exploiting its natural resources." If such a resolution were overwhelmingly approved it would probably be given legal effect. Such a resolution would not resolve any of the issues about the kind of regime that should govern the exploitation of the seas: in principle, it would not, for example, prevent the United Nations from throwing the resources open to national competition. But it would give to the General Assembly effective authority to determine the legal regime under which the resources should be exploited. Some states at least—probably including the United States and the Soviet Union—would be reluctant to give to a two-thirds majority of the Assembly full power to dispose of all the wealth of the sea, and to make law regulating extensive mining operations and impinging on other uses as well. Those concerned for freedom for military uses at sea will be particularly determined not to give to the United Nations so much authority, likely moreover to expand.

On the other hand, the General Assembly might here follow the precedent of outer space and declare that the seas (including the seabed) are not subject to national acquisition and sovereignty. Such a declaration, if accepted overwhelmingly and without opposition by major powers would be deemed declaratory of existing law and have great weight; as with outer space, it might later be put into a treaty. Such a legal principle would prevent states from acquiring parts of the seabed. It would not necessarily bar states (or their nationals) from proceeding to dig for resources under some theory that would analogize these resources to fish and the operating installations to vessels protected by the flag they fly, and subject to its law and to general principles of international law.

The United Nations and particularly the General Assembly play a different role when they proceed to study the problems and promote new law to be adopted by nations, probably at an international conference. This process began in December 1967 when the Assembly created an Ad Hoc Committee of 35 states. The Committee is to study the scope and various aspects of the agenda item proposed by Malta entitled "the question of the reservation exclusively for peaceful purposes of the seabed and the ocean floor, and the subsoil thereof, underlying the high seas and beyond the limits of present national jurisdiction, and the uses of these resources in the interest of mankind." See General Assembly Res. 2340 (XXII), Dec. 18, 1967.

INTERNATIONAL REVENUE—Behind many proposals to give the United Nations sovereignty in the seabed, or other special rights in regard to its resources, is a desire to obtain revenue for international purposes. In fact, the possibility of revenue does not depend on who owns the seabed or even on the kind of legal regime that governs the exploitation of its resources. (It has been suggested that international revenue might be obtained from other uses of the seabed, for example, by charging a fee to those who would use it for various military installations.) Even under a regime by which states are free to occupy the seabed or take its resources, there is nothing to prevent them from agreeing to make some payment to some body for some purpose. Some have expressed the fear that any revenue for international purposes would require an inspection-collection system by an international bureaucracy that would impinge on military uses of the seabed as well. This fear seems exaggerated: states are not likely to "cheat," and there are sophisticated means for assuring the revenue.

Revenue proposals range from modest plans for a small "tithe" for the United Nations to more ambitious schemes to appropriate and dedicate all the untold wealth of the seas to the heroic task of creating a welfare international society in which the gap between developed and developing nations, between rich and poor, would be sharply narrowed if not eliminated. Most proponents of any of the suggestions recognize that major revenue from the sea is not an immediate prospect. Any fees imposed must be modest so as not to render mining uneconomical or otherwise discourage entrepreneurs. For some time, then, income from any international "tithe" might barely cover costs of collection and other administration. But in some years, many believe, "royalties" from mining in the seas could produce huge sums.

The amounts that may be involved are not unrelated to the purposes to which they might be applied. Some have suggested that revenue go to the United Nations for its general purposes. In time this could resolve the finance issue that has threatened to tear the Organization apart and once brought its activities to a standstill. It could eliminate the United Nations' chronic deficits and give it the capacity even to expand its activities. It would remove the special burdens borne particularly by the United States, the largest contributor for all purposes, and make the United Nations independent of these American contributions, in time perhaps of all national contributions.

Assuming that states are prepared to accept the principle that the sea's resources should provide revenue for some international purposes, it is not likely that they will agree to give to the United Nations amounts that would make it largely independent of member contributions. Some countries, notably the United States which bears the major burden of financing the United Nations, recognize that such burden also makes the United Nations dependent on them and gives them corresponding power and authority in the Organization. They would be unwilling to give to majorities the means to go off on what they consider frolics, or worse. They might, then, be willing to see the United Nations get a "cut" only if it were a small one, or if United Nations spending were subjected to veto, weighted voting or some other limitation on majorities.

On the other hand, countries generally might be willing to see revenues from the sea go into a development fund, or be earmarked for special welfare purposes, some even related to the sea, *e.g.,* desalinization programs, sea research, development of new food resources from the sea. Here, too, even if substantial revenue should be realized, there will be issues as to the desirability, feasibility or wisdom of various programs not unlike those that have beset multilateral and bilateral aid and development programs in the past.

NATIONAL V. INTERNATIONAL REGIMES—Whether new law is made through the U.N. or otherwise, there will be differences as to whether it should be a "national" or an "international" regime. While these terms are hardly clear in definition and content, in general, national regimes suggest substantial initiative and autonomy for states and their nationals, subject perhaps to agreements among them for cooperation, for avoiding conflict and settling disputes. International regimes suggest important control by international institutions and at least some revenue for international purposes. But the concepts, the categories and the approaches are not mutually exclusive, and each can be varied by adding elements from the other, resulting in "mixed systems."

International operation—States could be wholly excluded and mining the seas could be confided to an international authority. Such a plan would eliminate the possibilities of international conflict and the need for a complicated regulatory system. But it would require a mammoth organization with a large staff of skilled personnel. It would put an international authority in Big Business in competition with national enterprises. There would be serious effects on world trade in minerals, and consequent economic and political difficulties. It seems neither desirable, feasible, nor acceptable and is not being "pushed" seriously.

International licensing—There have been numerous proposals that states be required to obtain a license from an international authority. Except for this common element, the proposals differ as to the character and composition of the international authority, the discretion it would have to grant or withhold a license, and the principles that are to guide its discretion. The authority might issue licenses on the basis of competitive bidding, to the first applicant for an area, or on some other principle of allocation and preference. A body with discretion as to when and where to permit exploration, to which applicants and for what minerals, would have important political and economic power. At the other extreme some contemplate a body that would issue licenses virtually automatically to the first applicant in an area, and collect a fee.

"Homesteading"—The basic national regime would permit any state to stake out a claim to explore an area of seabed when and where it will. By agreement, nations could add regulation of other kinds: *e.g.*, they might establish an international registry where a state could record its claim to operate an area. Registry would confirm the rights of a state against intrusion and challenge for at least a number of years. Registration might require payment of a fee. Eventually it might be necessary to develop a code of mining regulations to deal with the procedures for effectively making a claim: the size of a single "stake" and a "safety-zone" around it; the term for which it is valid; circumstances in which it might be forfeited—say, for non-prosecution; possible limitation on the number of claims by one state. I do not dwell on a suggestion that by a new agreement, the seabed be divided among the coastal states as though it were continental shelf—basically the "international lakes" proposal mentioned above. This would simplify operations, avoid competition and conflict, and any need for complex laws, agreements or institutions. But it would be obviously unacceptable, even to many of the coastal nations. Generally, nations would see no justification for such a proposal as applied beyond the areas where coastal states have any special rights or relevance. Some may see in it a threat to freedom of the seas for other uses as well.

International regimes would of course require international institutions but there is no doubt a role for international institutions in the implementation of any new law for the sea's mineral resources. Of course, an international authority with a monopoly to exploit these resources would look very different from one established to license exploitation by states. A licensing authority itself would be composed very differently if it had wide discretion or if it had merely ministerial functions. There is room for international institutions even in what is basically a "national system"—to run and monitor a registry, to collect fees and apply them to agreed purposes, to develop and recommend to the states a sea mining code, to police such a code after it is adopted, to settle disputes.

INTERNATIONAL ORGANIZATION

Some see in the oceans a unique opportunity for a radical departure in international relations. In the seas, they hope, it may be possible to rise higher above national egoism and to establish supranational authority to govern the seas for the common good: a new international organization might be established to determine and regulate all the uses of the seas.

Many will find such an all-embracing international authority to be not workable, acceptable, or desirable; yet they may see the need of lesser international institutions for particular purposes. I have suggested international machinery to regulate a new regime for the resources of the deep seas. There is a need for international organization to replace, subsume, or coordinate the many slivers of cooperative effort in scientific research and in weather prediction or modification. There are suggestions for a world oceanographic organization to explore the oceans. It is probably desirable to reexamine and revise existing institutions dealing with the conservation of living resources and the allocation of fishing rights in various regions. Agreed arms control might also require implementation by new international organization.

The organization of any international institution depends directly on the functions that it is to serve. In every case it would be necessary to decide anew whether there shall be executive, legislative, judicial, and administrative functions, and how these shall be distributed; whether nations shall have equal voice, or whether there should be some form of weighted voting; whether membership in particular bodies shall be based on the equality of nations or on particular qualifications. There are various models for international organizations already in existence; it will not require much imagination to vary these to reflect new needs. In every case it will be necessary to decide whether there shall be a new organization or a revision of an old; whether an organization should be independent, or part of an existing framework—say, part of the United Nations or the U.N. system of specialized agencies.

* * *

The law of the sea is changing and will probably change faster in the years ahead. Increasing uses require increased regulation. The rights of the coastal state need to be clarified. The continental shelf must have an end. Competition in fishing ought to be regulated and fish conserved, freedom of scientific research reasserted, military uses controlled. Most important, perhaps, there is a wealth of treasure in the sea for future generations, and decisions have to be made that will determine how those resources will be exploited, for whose benefit, with what consquences for individuals and nations.

Governments are beginning to think of these questions and to formulate policy in the light of national interests as they see them. For any nation, the relevant interests are not single or simple. For the United States, for example, desirable law for resources must take account of American interests in minerals, in the opportunities for American investors, in the early, economical and orderly exploitation of resources, in the possible effects on the world market in minerals and on the economies of particular nations. The United States must take account, too, of the impact of resources law on its multivaried interests in the sea. It must see resources policy in the context of a total national policy including our global interests, our concern for security, peace, order, and general welfare, our policies toward the United Nations, our attitudes about foreign trade and aid and development, our interest in some redistribution of wealth among nations and narrowing the divide between rich and poor.

Other nations also have competing interests, and the balance of interest of different nations might point to different law. Most nations of the world are coastal nations, tempted to extend their sovereignty seaward. But there are nations without coasts and not all coastal nations are equally blessed with plentiful offshore resources. Even those who would like a wide shelf for themselves may be unhappy with the consequences of letting others have one. A few nations do, while most nations do not, have the skills and the capital to reach for the resources of the deep sea. But some nations that do not have the technology might be able to "buy" it, or to "sell" their flag to foreign entrepreneurs. Most nations are poor and will want law that will enable them to share in the wealth of the seas, but many of them depend in many ways on rich and skilled nations who may wish a law of free enterprise and competition. Majorities will not wish to impose law that will discourage exploitation and, in any event, they cannot impose on the powerful, wealthy and skilled few, law that the latter cannot or will not live with.

New law for the deep sea is law for a long future. It should not be made too fast or too early, but basic principles and general directions are being determined now. Law, moreover, is made by the actions of nations as well as by formal procedures, and by inaction as well as by action; undesirable law should not be allowed to "happen," by default. The United States has to decide whether it wants a narrow or wide shelf, whether it wants competition at sea, whether and to what extent it will join in a grand effort to dedicate the sea's resources to meet the challenge of world poverty. Having decided, it must act in ways that will achieve it, avoid taking actions—and challenge actions of others—that are inconsistent with it. Specifically, for example, if it wishes a narrow shelf, it cannot grant leases that depend on a wide view of the shelf, and it ought not to allow others to do so unchallenged. If it desires an international regime for the deep sea, it cannot proceed to assert national rights or allow others to assert them there.

No nation, not even the rich and powerful United States, can get exactly the law it wants. But in the development of new law, American attitudes are critical. It has extensive coasts, capital, technological skills, power, influence, and a foreign policy that is in many ways enlightened. It has a unique opportunity to help develop law in its interests and for the common good.

Eugene B. Skolnikoff

3

National and International Organization for the Seas

International Organization

The development of international institutions and machinery for the seas is inextricably tied to the development and changes in the law of the seas. Quite clearly, the international agreements reached with regard to such things as ownership of the resources of the deep sea bed, regulation of world fisheries, and distribution of revenues acquired from exploitation of ocean resources, will determine many of the functions to be performed by international machinery. In turn, functions will influence the degree of authority and responsibility that must be accorded international bodies, and will determine patterns of international decision-making.

The substantive issues involved, and some of the legal alternatives have been discussed in the previous chapter. However, other dimensions are relevant. Important political and organizational questions must be taken into account in constituting international institutions, questions that in turn interact with legal considerations.

NEW TECHNOLOGIES AND INTERNATIONAL INSTITUTIONS

Perhaps the most important of these other dimensions is a general one that arises from a broad view of the impact of technology on inter-

EUGENE B. SKOLNIKOFF *is associate professor of political science at the Massachusetts Institute of Technology and head of the Science and Public Policy program here. In 1958–1963 he was on the staff of the Special Assistant to the President for Science and Technology. Dr. Skolnikoff is the author of* Science, Technology and American Foreign Policy.

national relations. Increasingly, new technologies are emerging that require the participation or cooperation of many countries if the benefits of the technology are to be realized, or that have effects beyond national borders, or that are relevant primarily to areas outside national jurisdictions, or that require investment beyond the means of most or all nation-states acting individually.

These technologies, which can be thought of as global technologies, are represented, for example, in aspects of outer space applications, in nuclear energy, in the possibilities for weather modification, in concern over air pollution, and, of course, in many elements of exploitation and use of the marine environment. These global technologies, which are likely to become more prevalent as man's ability to control and influence his environment continues to advance in scale and degree, have the general effect of reducing a nation's freedom of action to apply science and technology as it alone sees fit, even at times within its own borders.

One way to look at the situation is to recognize that the steady advances of technology are forcing a physical internationalization of the world beyond anything previously encountered. This phenomenon may not be different in kind from the internationalization resulting from economic and political interdependence, but in fact it may have different and new implications, especially in combination with economic and political interdependence, that bring about a fundamentally new situation. When it becomes technologically possible for one or a few nations to alter the entire earth's environment, perhaps irreversibly, or to destroy resources known to be needed by others, freedom of unilateral action may simply become unacceptable. And limitations upon unilateral action will be particularly relevant as technology becomes simpler and less costly, and spreads from a few advanced nations into the hands of many.

The development of international machinery to match this physical internationalization can, of course, take many forms, ranging from simple bilateral agreements to the creation of supranational institutions to which jealously guarded national prerogatives are delegated. If, however, there is a lesson to be learned from this concept of a trend toward global technologies it is that as new machinery is designed, or existing machinery extended, for example, to perform functions related to the oceans, nations must keep the larger picture in mind and recognize that they must build an international regime able to cope with more than just a series of isolated requirements. The precedents established now, the patterns of international operation allowed to develop, the fundamental strength and viability of international organizations, are all critical elements not just to determine a regime for the oceans

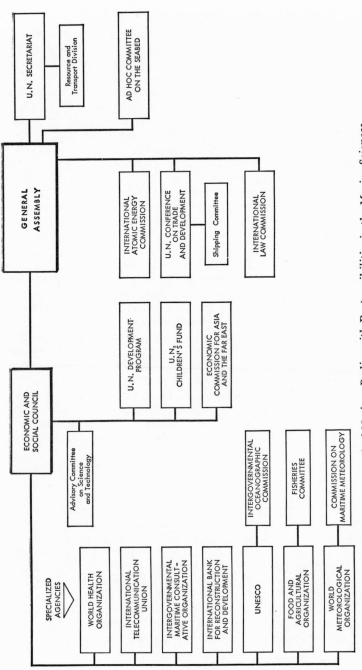

FIGURE 6. *United Nations Bodies with Responsibilities in the Marine Sciences.*

for the next few years, but in laying the basis for the future organization of an increasingly interdependent world.

EXISTING INTERNATIONAL AGENCIES

The issues associated with developing an adequate international regime for the oceans are made more complex because of the long history of private, national and international activities on the high seas, and the legal inheritance they bring. The same is true as far as organizations themselves are concerned. Almost every Specialized Agency of the United Nations has some involvement with the oceans, to say nothing of regional organizations, non-U.N. bodies such as Fisheries Commissions, and non-governmental bodies. Figure 6 shows the major U.N. bodies with responsibilities in the marine sciences, and gives an indication of the number of different organizations involved in the U.N. family alone.

International scientific cooperation first became significant in the beginning of the twentieth century when the Scandinavian countries united to support a single ship for joint use. But the first extensive multi-national cooperative investigation of the oceans came about as part of the International Geophysical Year organized by the International Union of Geodesy and Geophysics in 1957. This success led to the formation of the Special Committee on Oceanic Research (SCOR), which took advantage of the momentum gained in international cooperation to organize a study of the Indian Ocean. Twenty-three countries, with over 40 ships, participated in 180 cruises from 1959 to 1965 in what became known as the International Indian Ocean Expedition. By this time, nations realized that cooperative oceanic studies required coordination on a more formal basis, rather than by a non-intergovernmental group such as SCOR. Accordingly, UNESCO established the Intergovernmental Oceanographic Commission (IOC) in 1960. This Commission eventually took over the coordinating function of SCOR for the Indian Ocean Expedition and further, it organized other cooperative programs in the Tropical Atlantic, Kuroshio Current off Japan, Caribbean and the Mediterranean. During the formative years, the Commission was preoccupied with the coordination of international programs and the exchange of scientific data. More recently it has changed its emphasis to include problems of marine pollution, assistance to less-developed countries and the legal aspects of research and exploitation.

The form and purpose of the various international and regional organizations varies enormously. The U.N. Specialized Agencies generally view their individual involvements in the oceans from the perspective of their primary purpose, whether it be health, agriculture, or meteorology. UNESCO's interest is primarily the advancement of the science of the oceans, largely through the IOC. The U.N. family is involved in economic assistance programs related to the seas through the International Bank for Reconstruction and Development (the World Bank) and the U.N. Development Program; and in studies of problems associated with the oceans. The Ad Hoc Committee on the Seabed set up by the General Assembly (Res. 2340) in 1967, represents a major attempt to come to grips at a high political level with broader issues involving the oceans.

Outside the U.N. family, regional bodies, such as NATO and the Organization of American States are interested in expanding research and development related to the oceans, or in exploiting the resources of the oceans for the benefit of member states. Fisheries commissions are organized normally on a regional basis around the problems of specific fish or mammal varieties. For example, there is a North Pacific Fur Seal Commission, an International Pacific Salmon Fisheries Commission, and an International Whaling Commission (and others: see Table 8 in Chapter 1).

A variety of organizations function outside formal government channels. In the scientific field, the Special Committee on Oceanic Research of the International Council of Scientific Unions is the primary coordinating mechanism for the world's scientists and acts as advisor to the IOC. In a sense, multinational industrial companies can also be considered to be international organizations with interests in the oceans.

The variety of organizations, and of their interests, makes it hard to generalize about the international machinery concerned with the oceans. One characteristic does stand out: none of the existing machinery has effective regulatory or enforcement power. Even the fisheries commissions, which come close, are basically inter-governmental consultation and coordinating mechanisms with no real power to enforce decisions. The World Bank, in effect, has some enforcement power through its ability to withhold funds, but this has been of little significance with regard to the oceans.

Beyond this one generalization, there is little that can be said that applies to all the organizations. Some analysts have noted a pattern in which those organizations whose procedures allow executive action through some kind of governing committee of limited membership, instead of a one-country one-vote governing body, are apparently more effective and less bureaucratic. (The International Atomic Energy Agency, IOC and World Bank are examples.) This is not a surprising conclusion, but one that may not be applicable to all functions that must be served.

NEW PATTERNS

It appears quite clear that sooner or later it will be necessary to devise international machinery for the oceans with genuine regulatory power. Those concerned with fisheries warn us that it is essential to devise means to apply conservation measures to world fisheries; if we delay substantial losses in fish resources will occur (the whaling industry for example already is near extinction because of poor conservation practices). The problem is not for the future but is with us today: there is enormous physical and economic waste at a time when the world is desperately short of protein resources.

For mineral resources as well, some kind of international control and regulation will be necessary to carry out and enforce whatever agreements are eventually reached with regard to ownership and distribution of the nonliving resources of the sea. This could vary from minor international licensing authority, to ownership of the ocean bottoms with responsibility for regulating use, limiting entry and distributing revenues.

The small island nation of Malta has focused new attention of all member states of the United Nations on the international control and regulation of ocean bottom resources by a specific proposal: that by treaty the seabed . . . beyond national jurisdiction, shall be reserved for peaceful purposes in perpetuity; that the economic benefits from the exploitation of the seabed beyond present national jurisdiction shall be used to promote the development of poorer countries; and that the seabed beyond the limits of present national jurisdiction is not subject to appropriation in any manner whatsoever.

However, international machinery with substantial regulatory and enforcement powers will be the hardest to devise, for it would involve a degree of sacrifice of assumed national rights not yet acceptable. In addition, as with national regulatory machinery, there would have to be concomitant provision for judicial review and for representative machinery able to alter the terms of reference of the regulatory body.

Undoubtedly, any attempt to attack the regulatory problem head-on in traditional areas of national activity in the oceans, such as fisheries, would maximize the national resistance. One possible approach is to separate the "new frontiers" in the oceans—the deep sea bed—from the traditional problems, and create a new international organization (not necessarily in the United Nations but at the least associated with it) built around the exploration and exploitation of the deep sea bed. In time, such an organization could develop regulatory functions based on its knowledge and expertise, with nations willing to grant it some form of enforcement power because it is operating in areas where there are no prior vested interests. Eventually, if successful, the responsibilities of such an organization could be extended to regulation of some of the traditional activities in the oceans. Obviously, if vested interests are to be avoided, early action is required.

In the interim, it is clear that the existing means for encouraging conservation of living resources of the seas are inadequate, and some means, even if more extensive voluntary arrangements on a regional basis, will be required to meet the world's present and future needs.

Other pressures also exist for the development of new international organizations concerned with the oceans. The plethora of existing U.N. activities has led to a call for some kind of coordinating mechanism within the U.N. structure, perhaps located within the U.N. Secretariat. Another approach, not necessarily in conflict, would be the creation of a World Oceanographic Organization, or an International Ocean Agency to bring together in one organization all of the U.N. ocean activities, and particularly those of a scientific nature. Such a body could also be vested with the rights to the resources of the ocean beds as may be agreed to in the future, and could be the agency that was designed gradually to develop regulatory power in new areas of interest, as noted earlier.

There are other issues relevant to the development of international machinery for the oceans: for example, the role of international agencies in arms control agreements that may be reached, and their possible role in protecting the security of coastal states while encouraging development and use of the ocean's resources. Also, the importance of creating an environment conducive to investment of private and national resources in the oceans is an obvious prerequisite to the realization of the benefits of those resources, and must be considered in developing or extending international machinery.

This leads to a point relating to manpower, one that is often overlooked. The inevitable growth of international machinery in the marine environment will not only enlarge greatly the need for competent personnel to man those organizations, but will also place an additional burden on the U.S. manpower required to attend international meetings, represent government positions in bargaining sessions, develop American policy, and so forth. This may appear to be a minor matter, but in the light of the importance of individual competence to the successful operation of organizations, or to the effective representation of the nation abroad, it is likely to be a major problem. And if this proves to be a difficult problem for the United States, it can be imagined what it will mean to small countries.

In fact, one of the major objections today to strengthening international organs and giving them greater responsibilities is the loss of program quality that often results because of reduced efficiency and staff competence. If this situation cannot be changed over time, it becomes a powerful deterrent to any policy designed to strengthen international organizations for effective operation on ocean problems.

National Organization

The federal government's activities and responsibilities in the ocean environment have grown over the years as a series of pragmatic responses to specific needs. The needs were almost invariably defined in terms of the objectives of a typically rather narrow segment of American government or American industry. Since the oceans affect so many elements of government interest, a large number of government agencies and departments developed programs related to the oceans, most of them with little or no connections to each other. For example, 24 different bureaus of 11 federal departments and agencies are represented on the National Council on Marine Resources and Engineering Development.

This plurality of independent effort may have been acceptable when programs were small, but quite clearly as R & D efforts in the oceans expand, some form of general policy mechanism has to be created. Moreover, as ocean technology develops and the legal, military and regulatory issues discussed in earlier chapters become of great political concern, the need for effective policy machinery, perhaps including reorganization of existing patterns of operation, becomes steadily more pressing.

THE INTERAGENCY COMMITTEE ON OCEANOGRAPHY

The first formal policy and coordinating mechanism was that established in 1959 under the Federal Council for Science and Technology (FCST) in the Executive Office of the President. At first called the Subcommittee on Oceanography, it later adopted the title Interagency Committee on Oceanography (ICO). The Federal Council, a subcabinet committee of policy-level officials responsible for agency programs in science and technology, was at that time in the office of the Special Assistant to the President for Science and Technology, who also served as Chairman of the Council. In 1962, that office was reorganized as the Office of Science and Technology (OST), and the Federal Council became the chief coordinating arm of OST. The director of OST serves as Chairman of the FCST.

The ICO served the useful and essential functions of providing a forum for improved communication among Federal agencies, facilitating exchange of information and coordination, and undertaking the

first attempts to develop national programs in oceanography responsive to broad national needs and opportunities.

But the ICO was an interagency committee, with all the attendant
strengths and weaknesses of such committees. In particular, it had no
formal authority to control programs; what power it had within government stemmed from the influence of OST, and the desire of the
Bureau of the Budget to use the ICO as a means of overseeing the
entire federal oceanography program. It operated at a level of government several steps from the top, however, and as such was not in a
position to exert strong leverage on powerful agencies. In addition, it
had only limited capability of its own to evaluate programs and needs,
so that its program recommendations tended to be summations of
agency program plans rather than broader integrated truly national
programs.

The general feeling that federal government organization for marine
science affairs was not adequate to the task or the opportunities, led to
several attempts by the Congress during the 1960's to set up alternative
organization patterns. These ranged from a proposal to focus responsibility for a national oceanographic program in OST with the establishment of the post of Assistant Director of OST for oceanography (a
bill that passed the Congress in 1962 but was pocket-vetoed by President Kennedy) to the creation of a new Cabinet department concerned
with the oceans and the atmosphere. Many other proposals—variants
of these or wholly different—were made, but none was accepted by the
Administration until 1966.

CREATION OF THE MARINE COUNCIL

Finally, the Congress passed Public Law 89-454, the Marine Resources and Engineering Act of 1966, which the President signed on
June 17, 1966. The Law called for stimulation of scientific research,
accelerating development of marine resources; development of engineering capabilities to exploit the oceans; the encouragement of private
investment enterprise in marine science affairs; the advancement of
education and training in marine science; the utilization of this
knowledge for protection of health and property; the enhancement of
commercial transportation and national security; rehabilitation of
fisheries and improved utilization of resources; and finally, intensified
international cooperation.

The responsibility for implementation was assigned to a new National Council on Marine Resources and Engineering Development
located in the Executive Office of the President, with the Vice President
as Chairman, and including as members those Cabinet officers and
heads of independent agencies whose organizations have substantial

interest in the oceans. A civilian Executive Secretary, appointed by the President, was provided for the Council, and a full-time staff to aid in coordination and policy planning.

The act also provides for a citizens advisory Commission on Marine Science, Engineering, and Resources to be appointed by the President. The Commission is explicitly enjoined to submit a report to the President via the Council, and to Congress, that would include recommendations on national marine science programs and a governmental organization plan.

Probably the most significant organizational changes represented by the Marine Resources and Engineering Act were that it effectively raised the level at which marine science policy and programs are considered, that it provided for a full-time staff independent of the individual operating agencies, and that it looked formally to a prestigious Presidential Commission for long-term recommendations on organization and program. The Vice-Presidential Council mechanism resulted in increased visibility of oceanography in the work and studies reported in the two annual reports issues in 1967 and 1968 and in the increased resources allocated to the marine sciences.

In its operation, the Marine Council has relied heavily on its staff analyses of inputs from government agencies, and on a series of special interagency committees "to coordinate policies and programs and to develop recommendations as to issues requiring Council-level attention." [1] These committees are:

1. Marine Research, Education and Facilities
2. Ocean Exploration and Environmental Services
3. Food-from-the-sea
4. Multiple Use of the Coastal Zone

In addition, and most pertinent, the Secretary of State is responsible for another interagency committee on International Policy in the Marine Environment. The old ICO now reports to the Marine Council instead of the FCST, but has considerably diminished responsibilities.

ORGANIZATIONAL ISSUES

The relative success of the Marine Council in raising the level of policy debate and coordination in the marine sciences does not necessarily mean that it will or should continue as the primary focus of federal oceanographic activities. Many questions must be asked and answered before a preferred organizational plan can be designed. That

[1] The Second Report of the President to the Congress on Marine Resources and Engineering Development, *Marine Science Affairs—A Year of Plans and Progress* (Washington: U.S. Government Printing Office, March 1968).

is one of the major responsibilities of the Commission on Marine Science, Engineering and Resources, chaired by Dr. Julius Stratton, that was also created by PL 89-454, and which is supposed to submit its report on January 9, 1969. The Marine Council is scheduled to expire automatically some six months later on June 30, 1969.

MARINE BUDGET

In reviewing some of the questions that must be considered in designing an organizational plan, it is pertinent to keep in mind the gross expenditure on marine sciences and technology, which in fiscal year 1968 totalled close to $450 million and has been steadily rising. The total effort was broken up among many agencies and purposes. The Defense Department, and in particular the Navy, dominated the picture as measured in dollars, with a budget of $250 million, but three other departments and agencies—Interior, Commerce and the National Science Foundation—had budgets in excess of $30 million in the marine sciences. Moreover, actual budget size was a misleading measure of importance since programs of the greatest relevance to international legal, regulatory and control problems were represented by very small expenditures in other departments, such as the Agency for International Development, the Department of State, and the National Aeronautics & Space Administration.

CENTRALIZATION OR DECENTRALIZATION?

One of the important questions, however, was whether the U.S. marine sciences effort is excessively fragmented among different departments and agencies with consequent loss of symbiosis, political influence and systems planning capabilities, and perhaps unnecessary duplication as well. Concern that this was in fact the case led periodically to proposals for new combinations of existing agencies. The President's Science Advisory Committee (PSAC), for example, proposed in 1966 the centralization of much of the non-Navy oceanographic programs in a new environmental sciences agency (combining the Environmental Science Services Administration, Geological Survey, oceanographic activities of the Bureaus of Commercial Fisheries and Mines, and a portion of the Coast Guard's oceanographic activities).[2] Such a new agency could be independent—a sort of "wet NASA," or tied to an existing Department.

Other combinations or clustering were clearly possible, and assuredly

[2] "Effective Use of the Sea," *Report of the Panel on Oceanography of the President's Science Advisory Committee* (Washington: United States Government Printing Office, 1966).

no single proposal could solve all the relevant problems. For example, much of the Navy's R & D in the oceans in 1968 was directly related to civilian use. If in the future the Navy work is detached and tied to a new agency, military objectives are likely to suffer; if it remains outside, coordination remains a problem; if the clustering is done so as to place civilian programs under the Navy, civilian objectives are likely to suffer and other political concerns are raised. Similarly, even combinations entirely outside the Navy as suggested by PSAC will raise important questions about the relationship of R & D programs to the missions of existing Departments. The Departments of Interior and Commerce, for example, will have to have some realistic role in setting the objectives of R & D in the new agency since they will need the results. If such participation in setting of objectives is poorly performed, and historically such cross-agency planning has never been easy in the U.S. Government, it will not be long before the Departments are pressing for their own programs once again.

A NEW INDEPENDENT AGENCY?

However, on balance it appeared in 1968 that some kind of new Federal agency was needed to give focus and strength to the U.S. oceanographic effort, and to provide a clearer focus of interest for the development of international policy for the oceans. The PSAC proposal was one attractive possibility; another was a proposal to build a new agency around technology as well. In 1968, much of the technological development related to the oceans was carried out by the Navy; valuable and important as that was and is, many believed the U.S. should also have a civilian agency interested primarily in civil objectives in technological development. Such a function could be a major purpose of a new agency.

In addition, and to relate technological development to specific missions, the new agency could have as its primary focus two missions: the development of marine resources, and the protection and improvement of the environment. The latter, in particular, would serve to bring in more general environmental concerns along the lines of the PSAC report. Other missions could also be added according to what is politically and practically feasible, but these would provide the essential nuclei.

The creation of such an agency, which should be an Independent Agency not tied to an existing Department, would necessarily involve some amalgamation of existing activities in disparate Departments into the new agency. However, it would be neither possible nor desirable to combine all oceanographic-related programs in one place. In particular it would be inadvisable to cut back the Navy program, or those programs more closely tied to other Departmental missions than to the oceans.

CENTRAL POLICY PLANNING

Thus, even the creation of a new agency, whether along these lines or others, reduces but does not eliminate the need for central policy planning and coordination. Such policy functions can only be performed independently of particular departments or agencies, and that means, in effect, at a point in the structure above the departments. The Marine Council in the Executive Office of the President in effect did that. One possibility was for the existing Marine Council to be continued without any other changes, though a disadvantage of that course was the basic inter-agency nature of the Council, notwithstanding its high status and more-than-usual competence. Also in the long run, it is difficult for an Executive Office Agency chaired by the Vice President to maintain continued influence over cabinet departments. A President cannot establish for long periods a "czar" in any field, and especially not the Vice President (who does *not* serve "at the pleasure of the President"), if he is to retain effective cabinet secretaries and effective Congressional relations.

On the other hand, an Executive Office Agency can, with consulting and other analytical and planning help from private sources, maintain continuing planning and coordinating functions with limited power but considerable long-term usefulness. OST is an office which, for some science policy matters, has been successful over the long term in developing a useful and acceptable role of that kind in the Executive Office of the President.

Thus, long-term planning and coordination is possible at the Executive Office level and is a necessary component of organization for effective development of marine plans and programs.

The fragmentation, if it can be so described, in the Executive Branch in 1968 was paralleled by a similar fragmentation in the Congressional committee structure. Usually Executive Branch reorganization will induce some Congressional reorganization, but the political tradeoffs involved are a major factor in determining what can be realistically accomplished.

Organizational alternatives must take account of other issues as well. In particular, relations between the private and public sectors, and among all levels of government—local, state and federal, are of critical importance. What is the proper role of industry in exploitation of marine resources? What kinds of incentives and controls can be established to encourage rapid and economic use of ocean resources, while at the same time protecting the interests of the individual, the foreign policy interests of the U.S. government, and the legitimate interests of other nations?

Finally, how can American foreign policy interests be effectively represented in the marine science policy process?

All of the subjects discussed in this volume have direct relevance to American foreign policy. New ocean technologies alter the interests of nations in the high seas, or affect fundamental defense considerations, or change the importance of the oceans for economic development. International law, regulation and control are constant concerns of the nation's foreign policy makers. And the changing role of the oceans in military affairs is also a matter of foreign policy. The list can be extended to include potential arms control agreements, international cooperative research and activities of the U.N. family of organizations and others.

ROLE OF THE DEPARTMENT OF STATE

Quite clearly, the Department of State must have a major role to play in developing, coordinating, and recommending U.S. international policy with regard to the marine sciences and technology. It is much more than a coordinating job, for making sense out of the plethora of international programs and activities that exist is but one aspect of the task. Of much greater importance is the burden of the argument of the first part of this chapter: the need to look ahead and recognize that ocean technology, even more than outer space technology, is going to force internationalization, common effort and restraint on unilateral actions, all with potentially far-reaching political effects. Are the United Nations or the U.N. agencies able to carry out the role that will be forced on international mechanisms to manage the use of ocean resources? Will nations look to new Comsats for more efficient management? Or are new inventions required to accommodate differing political interests, avoid conflict situations and exploit marine resources efficiently and equitably?

The concern of responsible foreign policy officials may even extend farther. If they are interested in using marine science and technology as instruments for achieving long-range policy objectives, they must be in a position not only to prepare for and cope with new technology, but also in a position to participate in the setting of R & D objectives. Some technological developments may be more suitable than others for international management, others may have attractive arms control features, others may be of particular relevance to desirable patterns of development, and so forth. Such participation or intervention in technological matters is not easy outside the agency directly interested in the project, but when successfully done can have large foreign policy payoffs.

The responsibility for adequate representation of foreign policy interests in the marine sciences falls largely on the shoulders of the Department of State. No organizational arrangements in the government as a whole can alter that fact. A single agency primarily concerned with ocean policy could be a powerful stimulant, but it would make it harder for the State Department to stay abreast of the fast-moving field. The quality and competence of those primarily involved within the Department of State will be the most critical factor in how well the job is done.

At present, the Office of International Scientific and Technological Affairs in the State Department is the responsible office in the subject area. Their commitment, staff competence, and ability to work with the technical agencies of government that are actively advancing ocean technology and activities will be a major determinant of the creativity and intelligence with which the U.S. approaches the international challenges of the marine sciences in the years to come.

L. W. Martin and Hedley Bull

4

The Strategic Consequences of Britain's Revised Naval Role

A. THE BRITISH ROLE IN EUROPE—L. W. MARTIN

Great Britain's retreat from a global to a regional strategic role is a change of no little significance in maritime affairs. The retirement of a nation only recently demoted from being the second largest naval power in the world affects the naval balance in many areas. It also illuminates several strategic and economic aspects of modern naval affairs that affect even the super-powers.

REASONS FOR WITHDRAWAL

In its first three years of office, from 1964 to 1967, the Labor Government undertook a so-called "defense review," intended to produce a national military policy compatible with Britain's economic necessities. The economic case for retrenchment was powerful; in 1963 Britain had spent 7.2 per cent of its Gross National Product on defense, compared with French expenditure of 6.4 per cent and German of 6.2 per cent. Moreover, unless projected programs were cut, the trend would rise

LAURENCE W. MARTIN *has held the Chair of War Studies at King's College, London since October, 1968. Currently Woodrow Wilson Professor of International Politics at the University of Wales, Professor Martin has taught political science at several American universities. He has been a consultant on arms control to British and American government agencies and a contributor to professional journals. Professor Martin is the author of five books, including* The Sea in Modern Strategy.

rather than fall. Particularly serious was the heavy cost in foreign exchange imposed by overseas commitments. Exactly how the foreign exchange burden should be calculated remains a source of contention between the Treasury and the Ministry of Defense. It is roughly accurate to say, however, that, over and above some £90 million spent in foreign exchange in Germany, other overseas commitments consumed about £190 million in foreign exchange in 1966–1967, some £160 million of it going East of Suez.[1]

It was all too easy to attribute British balance of payments difficulties to this drain, whereas the true cause lay in the structure of the British economy. Nevertheless, overseas defense expenditure provided a ready way to bring about a relatively quick improvement by direct acts of policy, and the inclination to look to defense in general for remedies was reinforced by the high proportion of sophisticated British industry and of investment in research and development that was absorbed by military production. It was consequently not surprising that successive stages of the defense review brought progressively more decisive steps toward withdrawal from Asia.

Economy has not, however, been the only incentive contributing to withdrawal. A considerable body of influential British opinion has decided that military presence and intervention is no longer the best way to preserve Western political and economic interests in Afro-Asia, believing it to be frequently provocative and always costly. Even if the normal costs of a military presence are regarded as manageable, contemplation of the American plight in Vietnam, and of their own somewhat lucky escape from confrontation with Indonesia, has impressed upon British opinion the fact that a military presence entails an open-ended risk of escalation and indefinite expense. Moreover it must be recalled that the progressive contraction of British sovereign responsibilities East of Suez has also meant the steady erosion of the network of bases from which British military operations were traditionally conducted. Providing substitutes might well be both politically and financially difficult.

By 1966 such considerations had already brought the decision to build no more aircraft carriers and to rely after the mid-seventies on land-based air cover for naval operations. This entailed the surrender of the capacity for landings against powerful opposition and reliance upon the United States for support if ever operations requiring carrier support were contemplated.[2] Even if the money for new carriers had

[1] This is foreign exchange; the attributable total cost of the East of Suez commitments was over £300 million. See *Statement on the Defence Estimates 1966, Part II,* Cmnd. 2902, Annex H.

[2] *Ibid.,* Part I.

been available, the men to man them could not have been provided within Britain's system of voluntary service. Worsening economic conditions brought further amputations in July, 1967. Aden was already due for evacuation in January, 1968. Now British forces in Malaysia and Singapore were to be halved by 1971 and, by the mid-seventies, Britain was to leave its bases in the area altogether. After that she would honor her commitments in the area by a maritime presence and by a capacity for intervention and reinforcement by air.[3]

Not even this marked the end of retreat. Early in 1968, after devaluation, the intention to withdraw became complete. Evacuation was brought forward from the mid-seventies to 1971 and no more was heard of the maritime presence. The carriers would be phased out even more rapidly and the FIIIK would not be bought to provide long range air cover. Henceforth British defense policy would be centered upon Europe. Power beyond the European area would be confined to a vague "general capability." [4]

These progressive contractions have clearly been a strategic change of great magnitude. In purely naval affairs, the United States will soon be left alone as the only exponent of certain naval arts. In political terms it may find itself the only external interventionist power in parts of Afro-Asia. So far as Britain is concerned, revised defense planning as yet goes little beyond preparing the process of withdrawal. The task of constructing a positive strategy for Britain's new European role has scarcely begun. It is clear that the task will be particularly challenging for the Royal Navy which has hitherto been so preoccupied with affairs East of Suez and organized to a large extent around the now doomed carriers.

If the existing forces of the Royal Navy are concentrated in the NATO area they will constitute a fleet far larger than any other European navy. Thanks to an energetic program of building and scrapping escorts and submarines the quality of ships is also high; indeed in this respect the Royal Navy is considerably better off than the United States Navy, many of whose ships are overage and which has been severely strained by the Vietnamese war. But despite a natural tendency to draw comfort in a period of retrenchment from the size of the Royal Navy, it is obvious that uncertainties must surround the future of a fleet the traditional justifications for which have expired.

In the past there have been two main incentives for Great Britain to maintain a fleet much greater than those of nations so comparable in size as France and Germany. One of these, the existence of a large overseas empire and of distant strategic responsibilities, has just been

[3] *Supplementary Statement on Defence Policy,* 1967, Cmnd. 3357.
[4] *Statement on the Defence Estimates,* 1968, Cmnd. 3540.

decisively and, almost certainly, finally repudiated. The second, the peculiar dependence upon seaborne communications of an island nation, no longer enjoys unquestionable validity in the nuclear age. Certainly NATO strategy in general does not envisage a war prolonged to the point at which maritime attrition of the kind made familiar in the Battles of the Atlantic would play a substantial part.

Whatever the merits of this particular argument, the Royal Navy, and indeed all the naval forces of NATO, suffer from the three influences that undermine efforts to maintain a high level of military preparedness today: reliance upon the strategic nuclear alternative; reliance upon the contribution of other members of the alliance; and widespread disbelief in the imminence of war. For navies within the alliance, competing for limited resources, there is also the special problem that a fairly substantial contribution by the leading members of the alliance to land forces in Central Europe is sacrosanct as a device for ensuring the credibility of a united response to Soviet aggression. The Royal Navy thus faces problems that to a considerable extent exemplify those of other Western navies.

REMAINING MISSIONS

One must not allow the dramatic withdrawal from East of Suez to obscure the fact that, if Asia has provided most of the recent occasions for employing naval force in active operations, Europe and the Atlantic have always been potentially the more vital center of concern. Inspired by recent events to take a fresh look at the purposes of naval force in the NATO area, exponents of British naval strategy now identify several overlapping missions.

Major contingencies—So far as large scale general Soviet aggression is concerned, the task of the Western navies is seen as one of deterrence, not by meeting the threat fully, step by step, but by maintaining some ability to meet it at its own level and some ability to pose a risk of escalation. Thus while measures to counter Soviet strategic missile-firing submarines are regarded as necessary to impose costs on the Russians and to complicate their strategy, it is not regarded as a proper major concern at least of the European navies. This attitude cannot, of course, be divorced from the belief in Western Europe that once a nuclear exchange is initiated its effects will be beyond palliation, or from the appreciation that the Russians have a large land-based force targetted on Europe.

Following the same reasoning that military preparations should not concentrate upon contingencies which either are improbable or would, if they occurred, prove unmanageable, there is a decreasing inclination to anticipate the prolonged war on communications that once formed the centerpiece of NATO naval strategy. A third Battle of the Atlantic falls beyond the limits of what the British would regard as the threshold of all-out war in which such a battle appears irrelevant. In any case, to plan for it produces force goals as far beyond reasonable prospect of attainment as the 90 divisions of the Lisbon goals, with the consequent enervating effects that such unrealistic ambitions have upon the will to make any effort at all. This is not to rule out the possibility that, in some unforeseeable future, the Soviet Union might make limited attacks on Western shipping as a test of political will and determination. In such circumstances the NATO powers must be able to make a response in kind so as to impose a maritime equivalent to the "pause" so beloved of strategists upon the Central Front.

Such a response requires a sizeable defensive force, capable of action against surface and, above all, submarine or airborne attack. This doctrine of a pause relaxes the quantitative demands of anti-submarine warfare (ASW) from those posed by the traditional war of attrition. It does nothing to lower the technical standards demanded; indeed a high quality ASW force, unquestionably capable of rebuffing a limited attack on its own terms—that is, without marked escalation—so that the foe is obliged to contemplate a major onslaught, constitutes the best deterrent against the attempt being made at all. While it would be technically very difficult, given the pattern of seaborne trade, for the Russians to single out one or a group of the NATO powers for such attacks, in order to divide the alliance, there is some feeling that so far as possible the European members of NATO should possess a substantial capacity to mount a defense themselves, even though the fundamental framework of planning is for action within the alliance.

The advantages of and possible need for maritime action in support of the flanks of NATO is a natural concomitant both of certain trends in Soviet naval activity and of a general belief in NATO that concentration upon the vital but now probably stable Central Front may have led to undue neglect of the Northern and Southern extremities. Both the Scandinavian area and the Eastern Mediterranean offer opportunities for seaborne action, and the latter area at least is full of political unrest and uncertainty. Whether or not Soviet aggressive action is likely, there can be no doubt that the exposed members of NATO in those areas take such dangers seriously, feel somewhat neglected, and would welcome signs of allied concern. It is therefore desirable that, along with other measures such as provision for airborne reinforcement, the naval powers of NATO maintain and exercise a capacity for maritime intervention.

Both in Scandinavia and in the Aegean there are possible uses for an amphibious force, and the Royal Navy consequently envisages a continued role for its new assault ships, which were originally intended for use East of Suez. Western forces of this type could serve both to reinforce the flanks in periods of tension and to rebuff sizeable attacks in the event of an actual Soviet attempt to seize areas by *coup de main*. The contingency may be unlikely but the provision of earmarked defensive forces would compel the opponent to contemplate action on a much larger scale than would otherwise be necessary, with all the attendant risks. British naval opinion has thus welcomed the concepts of the NATO Standing Naval Force, of a Maritime Contingency Force and of a better working relationship than hitherto between SACEUR and SACLANT.

Additional tasks—While preparing to meet these major contingencies, the Royal Navy and, one hopes, the navies allied with it would be able to perform a variety of additional and almost certainly more frequently encountered tasks. Throughout the NATO area and perhaps beyond, they must afford a conspicuous naval presence to counter and offset the political advantages secured by the increasing activities of the Soviet Navy. From a purely British point of view, there is also, of course, political advantage to be secured from specifically British naval activity, contributing to British status and prestige in Europe, in the alliance and in the world beyond.

The Navy must also be prepared to protect British shipping wherever practicable, and, where desirable, to protect that of friendly nations. On an average day more than 600 British ships are East of Suez and to this number can be added over 500 ships of other NATO nations. More than 50 per cent of Western Europe's energy is imported by sea; the equivalent American proportion is ten per cent. Thus although a major war on shipping is unlikely except under conditions that are probably beyond management and certainly would elude British control, some capability for countering harassment of commerce remains a highly desirable asset.

Like all sea-girt countries Britain also needs to police its coasts and protect its coastwise trade and fishing fleets. Peering further into the future, technology promises to open up unprecedented commercial and military uses for the sea and its bed. Europe, with its wide continental shelf and crowded sovereignties, will experience to the full the complex questions of jurisdiction that such development must open and indeed already has opened up. It is possible that the considerable degree of economic integration underway in Europe will render such problems more tractable than in other areas such as Southeast Asia. Nevertheless British naval authorities are conscious of the need to pursue underwater technology to facilitate the surveillance, policing and exploitation of the seabed.

These are concerns inherent in maritime sovereignty; the more immediate strategic horizon of NATO is dominated, however, by the single problem of Soviet power. The steady growth of the Russian merchant marine and the progress of its navy toward greater strength and more ambitious operations has long preoccupied Western strategists. British observers have naturally not failed to perceive an acceleration of these developments in the last four or five years and to consider very carefully the changed pattern of operations, particularly in the Mediterranean, since the Arab-Israeli war of June 1967. As elsewhere, interpretations differ.

SOVIET NAVAL ACTIVITY

Soviet naval intentions would seem to have an importance beyond their intrinsic military significance, as an index of their future diplomatic policy and of their eagerness to disturb the existing political balance. Evidence of a highly enterprising maritime policy might be taken as some indication of aggressive political purposes. Thus to many observers increased Russian naval deployment far afield, particularly in the Mediterranean, the appearance of a modest amphibious element in that area, coupled with more talk of amphibious warfare in general, and a more energetic program of port visits, all combine to mark a new and more offensive policy. To this can be added Soviet interest in developing and exploiting port facilities in Alexandria, Port Said, Latakia, Hodeida, Berbera and Ras el Benares, and rumored interest in Mers el Kebir and even Malta, to parallel the network of refueling bases for aircraft also established in the Arab world. Such steps take place against a background of bolder claims for the utility of naval power made by Soviet naval leaders and can readily be fitted into a supposed strategy of outflanking the deadlocked Central Front, of filling the vacuum left by British retreats, and of penetrating areas hitherto regarded as Western preserves.

No responsible authority in Britain would deride this analysis or dissent from the view that Soviet naval activity is increasing and requires counter-measures. Nor could one deny that, naval questions aside, Soviet influence is insinuating itself deeper into the Middle East. On the other hand it is probably wise to consider that by far the greater part of contemporary Soviet naval activity could be depicted as a logical extension of familiar Russian naval policy.

Russia has been a major naval power for centuries, but has chiefly used her fleet not, like the Western powers, as a means for pursuing distant expeditions, but as a defense of the homeland in conjunction with land forces. Much of the recent extension of the range at which Soviet naval units are deployed would be necessary even to pursue this traditional role, given the greater distances from which enemy forces can project attacks upon the Soviet Union. Thus the Russian fleet has been drawn steadily outward, first to counter the threat from carriers, with aircraft of increasing range, later to meet the danger from Polaris and its successors. The Soviet fleet in the Mediterranean must be regarded at least in part as a somewhat belated response to the Sixth Fleet.

None of this is to deny that, since 1962, the Soviet Union has been providing itself, with whatever degree of deliberation, with an increasing capacity for long distance naval operations that provides it with an added range of options. Moreover, especially since the Arab-Israeli war of 1967 offered a perhaps unexpected illustration of the political use that could be made of such a capability, possibly encouraged by alarmed Western comment, Russia seems to be using her navy more deliberately as a source of influence. Neither the military nor the political challenge can be ignored by the West and British opinion regards an increased British naval presence in the Mediterranean as an early priority, preferably in conjunction with closer cooperative naval relations among the NATO powers most concerned. Such cooperative action perhaps on the model of the Standing Naval Force, might also be extended to the Indian Ocean if Soviet activity increases East of Suez. Joint forces, it is thought, might not only lighten the burden on the United States Navy, but also relieve the United States of some of the political disadvantages that a unilateral American military presence sometimes entails.

Consideration of the substantial traditional element in Soviet naval policy remains, however, a necessary corrective to alarmism that might provoke a hasty and exaggerated Western response. At the least it must be recalled that the Soviet Navy still retains its general war missions, that its forces, large though they are, may not be excessive for those tasks in view of logistical difficulties, and that consequently the strength available for political action and harassment bears little relation to the gross figures cited in uninformed surveys of the problem.

The British view is therefore that while a considered response should be made to serious Russian initiatives, it would be a mistake to try to match Soviet activity ship by ship, mission by mission. To do this would ensure the maximum effect of Soviet policy upon Western costs and would ensure Russia against wasted effort or error. Recent Russian naval policy has been full of costly mistakes, which it would have been an unnecessary extravagance for the West to counter in detail. NATO policy should therefore aim at offsetting the important *effects* of Russian policy and at denying it a completely free ride in any sphere. In this connection it is important to realize that the naval contest proceeds at two distinct levels, that of peace and that of war. A balance struck for one is not necessarily the best for the other. Thus if war comes the Soviet Mediterranean fleet is at present hopelessly outclassed by its foes, and would find it difficult to receive reinforcements. In peacetime, many of its purposes cannot be thwarted; there is no way to prevent Russia showing the flag. All that can be done is to ensure an active Western policy of the same kind. This, however, is unlikely to call for the same adjustments to Western deployment as an actual military inferiority would call forth. Thus the reactions appropriate to countering a pattern of peaceful action should not be confused with those appropriate to restoring a balance in combat.

FRENCH NAVAL COOPERATION

Consideration of the balance of naval power, particularly in the Mediterranean, is inevitably confused by doubt as to where the substantial French Navy stands. At present its professional attitude is more cooperative than the political posture of the French government would suggest. There are, of course, strong technical reasons for cooperation. The French Navy contains a number of American weapon systems—the Tartar, for instance—for which it requires logistical support. In the future it plans to fly the Anglo-French Jaguar. Without cooperation, tactical exercising would be difficult; this is probably why the French submarine force remained earmarked for NATO for some time after other units withdrew. Even today joint exercises are held and technological cooperation takes place, the latter being hampered by the French hunger for information on nuclear systems and the American refusal to supply or allow the British to supply it. Nevertheless the French nuclear program also encourages the French Navy to seek cooperation because it imposes dire shortages on French general purpose forces.

France has an obvious national interest in the security of certain areas of sea, particularly the approaches to her ports and to Francophonic Africa. The French Navy is therefore likely to continue ad hoc cooperation, to undertake contingency planning at a service level, and to try to maintain the physical means of communication and joint action. So long as the present regime lasts, however, this cooperation will be on French terms and will not be something upon which the NATO navies can place much reliance, particularly in the most probable circumstances of tension rather than war.

THE ROYAL NAVY

Against this background of thought, what will be the shape of the future British fleet? The lead time of naval systems ensures that most of the forces available for handling the contingencies of the next decade or more are either in existence, are building, or at least are in an advanced state of design. Luckily, as already remarked, much of the Royal Navy is fairly new and of high quality.

The carriers will almost certainly be gone by 1972. Without them, Britain's requirement for escorts will be reduced and of a somewhat different kind. More air defense will have to be shipborne and more attention paid to cooperation with land-based air cover. Helicopters of all kinds will play an increasing part in such roles as ASW, air-to-surface missile firing, and reconnaissance.

The number of destroyer-frigate types will probably fall from over 90 to about 70. This will be achieved by scrapping old ships, such as the Type 15, and pursuing so far as possible an active program of new construction. A new frigate is being designed to follow the modern, successful *Leander* class, and the large Type 82 destroyer, intended for carrier support, will be developed downwards into a new destroyer with area air defense (Sea Dart) to succeed the existing County class, and upwards into a new class of helicopter-carrying cruiser, to succeed the Lion class, capable of exercising elaborate command and aircraft control functions. This defensive force will be supplemented by an amphibious assault capability, at present supplied by the new *Fearless* and *Intrepid* (LPH), and by a force of fleet submarines (SSN). The role of the latter is seen primarily as an offensive threat to the Soviet Navy in its own waters, thereby imposing a heavy defensive investment on it.

At present the Royal Navy, by virtue of its supposed role East of Suez, has a great deal of modern equipment for long distance afloat support. It is hoped that this can be retained and renewed, making it possible not only to maintain forces in the Mediterranean without a fixed base (it is unlikely that Malta will be reactivated) but also to deploy a fleet anywhere in the world. Because the North Atlantic imposes standards of seakeeping as high as anywhere in the world, and because the Soviet threat is the most sophisticated that the British can meet, ships suited for the NATO role can, by the provision of modest climatisation equipment, confidently go anywhere. Thus the Royal Navy would retain the capability for a modest role East of Suez, but only, of course, upon receipt of some warning. The speedy reactions of permanent presence will no longer be attainable.

A description of the Royal Navy would not be complete without reference to the Polaris force, though this is clearly a task of a different order from the main concerns of the navy. For several years to come the Polaris force will remain a technically sound concept, while its political justification lies beyond the scope of this paper. Within a year or two, however, the British government will have to make decisions about the future of the force that may well affect the resources available to the Navy. Given the proliferation of missile defenses, the British force may need a new generation of warheads. The introduction of these and the over-all effectiveness of the force would be greatly facilitated and enhanced by the addition of one or two more boats. Alternatively the force could be abandoned now and the boats converted to the attack role. The decision will be affected both by the general climate of nuclear diplomacy and by the behavior of France, soon, perhaps, to be the owner of a second European force of missile submarines. The outcome will have important consequences for the British and French navies, but it is not, in any real sense, a naval decision.

The over-all principle underlying current British naval thought is that the Royal Navy should remain one that, while regarding its contribution to the Western alliance as its most important task and as the only way in which it can hope to master its chief problems, remains a self-contained force capable of independently performing the tasks for which it is technically equipped. Thus the intention is to maintain a balanced force and there is no thought of abandoning the provision of such essential components as command ships to other navies. The fluidity of the diplomatic situation and the length of time it takes to create a balanced force is thought to make this policy an essential insurance against an unforeseen future in which the present pattern of cooperation might not endure. This is a political equivalent to the emphasis on flexibility which is a central feature of British strategic naval doctrine.

There is here, of course, no present disaffection from the alliance or with the close cooperative relationship the Royal Navy enjoys with that of the United States. Indeed there are hopes that, in the coming years during which it is likely that both navies will face a period of stringent economy, a greater degree of cooperation in development, production and operations than ever experienced heretofore may ease the lot of both. But, whatever the pattern of future diplomatic alignments, Britain possesses in her Navy an existing and potential force that suits her diplomatic needs, her geographical position and her traditional skills.

B. Indian Ocean and Pacific Strategy
in the Wake of Britain's Withdrawal—Hedley Bull

Seapower exercised in the Pacific and Indian Oceans is a major instrument of U.S. policy in Asia. The exercise of military force on and under the oceans cannot be separated from its exercise on the land and in the air and space. Whereas even until the Second World War naval vessels had as at least their principal task in war the struggle with other naval vessels so as to gain command of the sea, the naval fleets of today, both surface and submarine, often have the chief function of attacking targets deep inland or in the air, and are themselves subject to attack from both these environments as well as from the oceans. It is, however, possible to distinguish the tasks performed for U.S. policy in Asia by that part of her military power that is deployed in the oceans that wash the eastern and southern shores of the continent.

ROLE OF THE UNITED STATES NAVY IN ASIA

First, naval forces in the area form part of U.S. strategic nuclear war forces and contribute to the fulfillment of their global role: the deterrence of strategic nuclear attack upon the United States and its allies by means of a capacity to produce "assured destruction" in the adversary country or countries, and the maintenance of a capacity for "damage limitation" in the event that such an attack takes place. The Polaris submarine force, now to be refitted with the Poseidon missile, provides a major component in America's "assured destruction" capacity, which is likely to increase in importance as the result of the threat represented by multiple and individually guided re-entry vehicles to the invulnerability of the land-based, fixed-site missile component. U.S. carrier forces in the area that are equipped with planes capable of striking at inland targets with nuclear weapons must also be reckoned to contribute to "assured destruction" capacity.

The "damage limitation" function of strategic nuclear war forces is presumably served by anti-submarine warfare forces in the area, inso-

HEDLEY BULL *is professor of international relations at Australian National University. He has been director of the Arms Control and Disarmament Research Unit of the Foreign Office, and has taught at Princeton University and the London School of Economics. Professor Bull is the author of* The Control of the Arms Race *and* Strategy and the Atlantic Alliance.

far as these are directed toward identifying and destroying Soviet nuclear missile submarines in the event of war; by a variety of intelligence functions performed by naval vessels in the area; by the possible use of the Polaris force itself in striking at enemy missile sites, airfields and other vital military targets. The United States may also in time provide itself with a sea-based ballistic missile defense system designed to intercept enemy missiles in the ascent stage.

Secondly, naval power in the Pacific and Indian oceans enables the United States to intervene militarily in local conflicts in the Asian area. The strategic nuclear confrontation between America and Russia, expressed as it is in the ability of the two giants to attack one another with unlimited force almost anywhere in the globe, has modified the historic principles of geopolitics or geo-strategy, but it has not eliminated them. Circumscribed and contained by the fear of unrestrained war, limited military conflicts continue; and at this level the United States finds itself, as it did during the Second World War, in the classical position of a maritime nation wishing to establish or defend its footholds in Eurasia and dependent in doing so on superior naval power.

Local military intervention in Asian conflicts may take the form simply of the deployment of forces in the area, intended to influence the course of a war without participating in it, as when the U.S. Seventh Fleet was interposed between China and Taiwan in 1950—or it may involve direct participation. It may comprise the "half-way house" of attaching military advisors to one side in a struggle, as in the case of the participation of United States advisors on the government side in the early stages of the war in Vietnam, or it may involve full participation as a belligerent. Such participation has taken the form of intervention in a civil war together with limited military action against another intervening state in Vietnam; and it has taken the form of the waging of a "classical," limited international war in Korea. There are other forms of local military intervention which have not taken place but the possibility of which is evident enough to exert an influence on the course of events: for example, the limited use of nuclear weapons in either a battlefield or a strategic role.

A basic presupposition of military intervention in Asia in all these forms is U.S. naval power. Whether military intervention takes the form of naval, land or air action, or of some combination of these, it must be transported to the area concerned. Professor L. W. Martin has distinguished three forms of "lift" of fighting formations that take place: introduction of forces into a hostile area by assault; introduction of forces into an area where at least an initial foothold already exists—

i.e., an "administrative" or "red carpet" landing; and the supply and maintenance of armed forces already established in an area.[5]

Airpower has made inroads on the traditional role of the navy in providing all three of these varieties of "lift," but naval forces appear to remain essential. The classic amphibious assault, executed by landing craft under the cover of naval guns and aircraft, as demonstrated during the Pacific campaign in World War II and at Inchon in 1951, has been modified by the new role of the carrier-based helicopter in amphibious assaults and by the growing range of land-based aircraft used in support of such assaults. But it still holds its own as against the very limited role so far for purely airborne seizure of hostile territory. Long range transport aircraft, with their advantages of speed and ability to bypass any hostile naval threat, now provide competition with naval transport in the "administrative" landing of fighting units and in the supply and maintenance of forces established in an area. But naval transport is still by a large margin the principal means by which U.S. forces and equipment are brought to bear in the Asian region; nor does it seem in danger of losing this position.

Thirdly, naval forces advance the purposes of U.S. diplomacy in the area in a variety of ways that stop short of the actual use or specific threat of force. The presence of U.S. naval bases and vessels is tangible evidence of American power in the area, inducing in allies and associates a sense of security, and in opponents a sense of respect, that cannot be provided by forces and weapons located in distant North America, however massive they may be and however speedily they may be summoned into the area.

These uses of naval power include the work of naval forces in the Pacific in connection with missile tests and space activities. They include the collation of intelligence. They include the demonstration that certain waters are international by the deployment of naval units in them, as has recently occurred in the Sea of Japan. They include "showing of the flag" by visits to friendly ports—perhaps designed to strengthen morale, or to convey a sense of U.S. capability to a nearby opponent, as in the case of naval visits to Hong Kong. They include the protection of commerce.

The fact that some of the threats against which U.S. naval power is directed seldom in fact materialise does not mean that the exercise of this power is without point. The deployment of military power in the Asian region has the purpose of engendering a sense of security against imaginary threats as well as against real ones. Moreover, were it not for the pervading presence of American naval supremacy in the Pacific,

---

[5] L. W. Martin, *The Sea in Modern Strategy* (London: Chatto and Windus, 1967).

certain threats—for example, to merchant shipping in time of peace or of limited war—which are now imaginary might become real.

THE BRITISH WITHDRAW

Throughout the postwar period a presupposition of U.S. policy in Asia has been a substantial British military presence in the area, based mainly, though not exclusively, in Singapore and Malaysia. British and U.S. policies in Asia, it is true, have sometimes been at loggerheads. During the late 1940's and 1950's U.S. attitudes toward British policy in Southeast Asia were still defined largely in terms of disapproval of colonialism. British attitudes toward U.S. policy, though qualified by recognition of America's paramount position in the area and by acceptance of the basic aim of resistance of Communist expansion, have been constantly critical of the methods of U.S. policy, as is exemplified by Britain's recognition of and trade with mainland China, her counsels of restraint during the Korean war and on the occasion of the French collapse at Dien Bien Phu, and her failure to provide more than qualified diplomatic support for the war in Vietnam. Despite these tensions the United States has recognized that while the British remained, a substantial area on the southeastern periphery of Asia could be counted upon to remain firmly within the Western orbit without requiring the United States to assume any burden. During the 1960's the United States put considerable pressure on the British government to maintain its position in the area; and this pressure played a major part in postponing the British decision to withdraw until 1967.

In retrospect this decision has the appearance, no doubt misleading, of inevitability. The Singapore base was constructed as part of the network of imperial defense. The greater part of the British Empire lay in the territories bordering the Indian ocean: South Africa, the east African colonies, Aden, the South Arabian and Persian Gulf protectorates, India, Burma, Malaya, Ceylon, Australia. Singapore guarded the approaches to the Indian Ocean from the Pacific, while providing a link in the chain that began with Gibraltar, Malta and Suez and stretched through the narrow seas to Hong Kong and other British possessions in the Pacific. Withdrawal from empire robbed Singapore and other links in the chain of their initial rationale.

For twenty years after the transfer of power in India other rationales were found. They included the desire to protect investments and trade in Malaya and Singapore, the desire to contribute to the global containment of communism, a recognition of the importance attached by Australia and New Zealand to a British presence in the area, the will to resist blatant aggression in the form of Indonesia's confrontation policy and, in the last few years, the need to accommodate British policy to strongly expressed American views as to what it should be. But perhaps most importantly, Britain was kept in Southeast Asia by a lingering imperial or post-imperial frame of mind, expressed not in any illusions that colonial control could or should be prolonged, but in sentiments of loyalty to local ruling groups with whom experiences had been shared; in a residual Commonwealth ideology in which the defense of India, Australia, New Zealand and other former dependencies still figured as an important goal of British endeavour; and by a sense (most noticeable during the period of Malaysian-Indonesian confrontation) of enjoyment in the unilateral, honorable and on the whole strikingly successful exercise of military power in a world in which the opportunities for such exercise of power by Britain had dwindled almost to vanishing point.

When the present Labor Government came to power in October 1964 British military force was deployed in Southeast Asia on a scale that had not been equalled since the Second World War, and the new government proceeded to define a world role for Britain in terms that indicated a turning away from the aspirations to a predominantly European role implicit in the previous government's 1962 bid to join the European Economic Community. But British policy by 1966 was moving rapidly toward the contraction of this world role. Chronic and recurrent balance of payments crises implied a need for cuts in overseas military expenditure, and on each occasion the maintenance of British forces in Germany was held to have priority. A few months after the change of government in Indonesia in September 1965, confrontation came to an end. The Commonwealth ideology, especially as the result of the bitter conflicts within the association that developed out of the Rhodesian declaration of independence, further declined; and the new ideology of "Europe" gained in strength, especially in the Labor Party where it had previously failed to capture the minds of the leadership. Disillusion with the feasibility and doubts about the morality of Western military intervention in Asian conflicts, as exemplified by the war in Vietnam, came to be expressed in left-wing hostility to the East of Suez commitment, but also in official suggestions that Western policy should at least aim at disengagement from the mainland of Asia, in favour of a "peripheral strategy" of influencing Asian affairs from secure island bases such as Japan, Australia and the Philippines.

The contraction of the "world role" enunciated in the Defence White Paper of February 1965 came in three stages. The February 1966 White Paper (Cmnd. 2901) made a series of qualifications to Britain's future military role outside Europe, and announced the decision that no more carriers would be constructed, thus causing the resignation of the First Sea Lord and the Minister of the Navy, Mr. Christopher Mayhew, who argued that no worthwhile role for Britain was possible East of Suez without carriers, and that the choice lay between abandoning an East of Suez role and maintaining the carrier force.[6] In July 1967 a supplementary White Paper announced that Britain would withdraw altogether (Cmnd. 3357) from Singapore and Malaysia by the middle 1970's, and that ground forces would be withdrawn from Aden and the rest of southern Arabia at the time it became independent at the beginning of 1968. However, the July 1967 document envisaged that naval and air forces would remain in the Aden area for a short time after independence, and it stated that after withdrawal from Singapore and Malaysia Britain would continue to make a "substantial contribution" to the Commonwealth Strategic Reserve in the area, presumably by naval forces cruising in the area or by air and ground forces based in Australia.

The final stage came with Prime Minister Wilson's statement in the House of Commons of 16 January 1968. The target date for withdrawal of forces from Malaysia and Singapore was brought forward to the end of 1971. British forces in the Persian Gulf area were also to be withdrawn by that time, after which no British military bases would remain outside Europe and the Mediterranean. Moreover, it was announced that after these withdrawals Britain would not maintain any "special military capability for use in the area," but would have only a "general capability" for deployment overseas. Force was given to this statement by the announcement that the order for 50 F-111 aircraft from the United States had been cancelled, that the existing carrier force would be phased out as soon as withdrawal was complete, and that reductions would be made in the rate of naval construction, for example in nuclear-powered hunter-killer submarines.

The British military presence in Southeast Asia has not brought any significant addition to American armed force in east Asia and the Pacific, where in the postwar world as in the closing stages of the Second World War the United States has had ample strength to act without Britain and has often preferred to do so rather than accept the compromises which close partnership in the area would have implied. For example, the United States overrode Australia and New Zealand in excluding Britain from participation in the Anzus Treaty, concluded in 1951. But presence in the area has helped to make Britain a sympathetic junior partner to the United States in the enterprise of containing mainland China, as exemplified by Britain's participation in the Korean War, her membership in SEATO, her cooperation with the United States in the planning of assistance in the defense

[6] See Christopher Mayhew, *Britain's Role Tomorrow* (London: Hutchinson & Co., 1967).

of India in 1962, and her joining with the United States and the Soviet Union in the declaration of 8 March 1968 announcing the willingness of the three countries to assist non-nuclear powers, signatories of the proposed Non-Proliferation Treaty, in the event that they are subject to nuclear aggression or the threat of it.

Moreover, in the Malay world and in the Indian Ocean, where Britain has remained the predominant Western power, the broader purposes of American diplomacy have been well served by British policy. The Communist insurgency of 1948–1960 was suppressed and power was transferred to stable, non-communist governments. Malaysia was defended against Indonesian threats and limited attacks during the period of her militant nationalism and cooperation with China, 1963–1966. The frustration of the "confrontation" policy by British arms probably contributed to the change of regime that took place in Indonesia in 1965. Finally, in the period since the secession of Singapore from the Malaysian Federation, the British presence has helped to ease relations between the two governments.

Seapower has played a vital part in the exercise of British power in Asia in recent years; indeed, there is a strong case to be made out for the view of Mr. Christopher Mayhew that without effective naval force in the area, a distant island such as Britain cannot bring any significant military influence to bear on it. As in the case of U.S. naval forces, the role of British naval power can be considered in terms of its contribution to strategic nuclear war forces; its function in local military intervention; and its utility in advancing the purposes of British policy by means short of war and the specific threat of it.

The contribution of the Royal Navy to strategic nuclear war forces is of course marginal when compared to that of the U.S. Navy. Nevertheless, some British carrier forces in the area are known to be nuclear-equipped; and together with the V-Bomber forces located in Singapore, Britain must be reckoned to have deployed in the Far East in recent years a capacity to strike with nuclear weapons at China or Indonesia. It is in fact most improbable that any British government either at that time or in the foreseeable future would have the will to order nuclear forces into action against one or the other of these countries on behalf of an ally. But it does not follow from this that British nuclear capability in the area has been without deterrent effect, for this is a matter not of what Britain would do, but of what her opponents believe she would do, which is very hard to judge.

The Royal Navy's force of four Polaris submarines, the first of which is going into commission this year, will become the chief instrument of British strategic nuclear power with the demise of the V-Bomber force. The present British government has given some consideration to the possibility of deploying this force in the Indian Ocean rather than the Atlantic, where it could strike at targets in both the Soviet Union and China. Since the British Polaris force is at present "committed to NATO," such a deployment would presumably require consultation with Britain's allies. An Indian Ocean deployment of the Polaris force would contradict the main present drift of British policy. If, as seems likely, an Atlantic deployment is chosen, it would still be possible to send British Polaris submarines to areas where they would be in striking distance of targets in Asia. But the evident decline of British interest in the area is bound to diminish whatever credibility has attached in the past to the idea of British nuclear action in Asia.

British military intervention in the area has presupposed sea lines of communication from Britain to the Indian Ocean via Suez and the Cape. Carrier forces took part in the re-occupation of the former east African territories in 1965, the landing in Kuwait in 1961, and the withdrawal from Aden in 1967. The defense of Malaysia and Singapore against "confrontation" involved extensive use of naval forces for patrolling the straits, and the provision of carrier-based air support.

British policy has been able to exploit naval forces in the Indian Ocean for the protection of British commerce which passed through the Indian Ocean; to provide a sense of security to other nations, especially Australia, which are dependent on Indian Ocean trade routes; to demonstrate interest in Commonwealth defense in exercises with the Indian, Pakistani, Australian and Malaysian navies; to protect her Indian Ocean dependencies, such as Maritius, and the Seychelles; and since 1966 to mount a naval patrol preventing the supply of oil to Rhodesia through the port of Beira.

After the end of 1971, when Britain will be without bases in the area, what likelihood will there be of her return in an emergency? Britain's continuing commitments may be readily identified. She proposes to remain in Hong Kong until the lease for Kowloon runs out, and in Fiji, where potential conflict between the Fijian and immigrant communities poses a familiar problem of decolonisation. She will remain a member of SEATO. For many years to come the sentiment will continue to be voiced in Britain that in the event of a threat to the security of Australia and New Zealand, Britain must repay the debt she incurred at Gallipolli and Tobruk by coming to their aid. There are, indeed, ties of trade, investment, migration, culture and common institutions that will preserve a special relationship between Britain, Australia and New Zealand for the foreseeable future, even though it will cease to be marked by dependence of the latter on the former.

Whether Britain will have the capacity or the will to make a reality of these commitments is less clear. In the absence of carriers and of the F-111 aircraft Britain will be unable to provide forces in the area with air support. She will have no naval bases of her own in the area; and South Africa has now threatened to revoke the 1955 agreement under which Britain is granted dockyard and refuelling facilities at Simonstown. The discussion that has taken place in Australia concerning British cooperation in the establishment of a naval base at Cockburn Sound in Western Australia has come to nothing.

Britain has a military air route to the Far East via Bahrain and Gan, but this is subject to the granting by Middle Eastern states of permission to overfly. South Africa has also recently threatened to deny overflying rights to Britain. In 1965 Britain grouped together a number of islands (Fanquhar, Aldabra, Desroches and the Chagos Archipelago) to form the British Indian Ocean Territory; and in April 1967 an agreement between the United States and the United Kingdom for joint use of the Territory was made public. The British project of developing in transit facilities at Aldabra, however, has apparently been abandoned. The likelihood is that the only secure air route from Britain to the Far East will be the west-about one via the United States.

EFFECT ON WESTERN INTERESTS OF NEW NAVAL
DEVELOPMENTS IN ASIA

Does the impending British withdrawal endanger Western interests in the area? Advocates of the withdrawal have denied this with the arguments that Western military intervention in Asian conflicts is politically counter-productive, and that by removing themselves from the scene the Western nations will afford their friends a better chance of surviving in their own countries; that only removal of the Western props that now sustain them will provoke local leaders into the efforts that can save them; that the only alternative to communist or militant nationalist regimes are military juntas or corrupt dictatorships which are or should be equally anathema to us; and that even if the worst should befall and these countries were to fall into hostile hands, the security of Western countries would remain unimpaired.

The actual position is more complex. Some Western interventions in Asian conflicts have defeated their own purpose but others, like the United States action in Korea and the British against the communist terrorists in Malaya, have achieved it. Withdrawal may prod local leaders to help themselves, but if they are not yet able to do so, it may be catastrophic, as in the case of the Belgian retreat from the Congo. Some non-communist regimes in Asia are authoritarian and corrupt but others, like the governments of Singapore and Malaysia, are not.

The spread of communism in Asia does not necessarily endanger the security of North America or Western Europe, and may accelerate the trend toward polycentrism in the world communist movement which has robbed it of its former force. But to assume that Western security will not be affected is a gamble; moreover, the West has interests not only in its own security but in the preservation of political orders linked to it by common values and mutual economic interest.

Whether military intervention in the Malay world and the South Arabian-Persian Gulf area is desirable or not, by the end of 1971 the established means of accomplishing it, viz. via a British foothold in the area, will have been removed. In the event of a resumption of Indonesian military expansionism, of hostility between Malaysia and Singapore, of the renewal of a communist insurgency of major proportions in Malaysia, of a Chinese communist bid for Singapore, of new patterns of disturbance which we cannot foresee, military intervention will have to be foresworn or accomplished by new arrangements.

Moreover, British naval power will have ceased to be a major factor in the Indian Ocean; and the consequences of this will have to be faced whether new provision is made for intervention on the Asian mainland or not. Singapore, where it is hoped that the naval dockyards will be taken over by commercial firms, and Aden, from which the British have already gone, may become naval bases in hostile hands. With the withdrawal of British vessels from the Indian Ocean, none of the littoral states (South Africa, India, Indonesia and Australia are the most important in terms of naval power) is at present capable of establishing anything more than local naval dominance.

One candidate to succeed the British in their naval role is the Soviet Union. Soviet submarines are presumed to be already active in the Indian Ocean, and to include both the hunter-killer type, designed to offset United States Polaris submarines and nuclear-armed carrier fleets, and the ballistic missile-firing type, an increasingly important component of Soviet strategic nuclear forces. There is evidence, moreover, that the Soviet Union is now developing naval power to support a military interventionary and general diplomatic role on the high seas, on the pattern of U.S. and British naval forces.

The Soviet Union is known to possess two helicopter carriers for amphibious assault. In 1964 her Naval Infantry was reactivated, and is now larger in numbers than the Royal Marines. Her fast-growing merchant fleet (the result both of increased overseas trade and of increased desire to carry it in Soviet ships) and her very large and modern fishing and oceanographic fleets, give her a stake on the high seas. As regards bringing her power to bear in the Indian Ocean she is handicapped by her complete lack of attack carriers and bases in the area, and by limited capacity to refuel at sea. There have been reports, however, that the Soviet Union is seeking the use of Indian port facilities in return for military and economic aid. The Soviet Union is at present equipping the Indian Navy with submarines, and has supplied cruisers, submarines and torpedo boats to Indonesia. Developments could quickly take place that would provide the Soviet Union with the use of port facilities in Aden or the Persian Gulf area. Admiral Gorshkov, the chief of the Soviet navy, toured Indian naval installations in February 1968 and has stated that the United States no longer has mastery of the seas.

It should not be assumed that any projection of Soviet naval power on the high seas is necessarily injurious to Western interests. The Soviet Union now has some important objectives in common with the United States and her allies, in placing obstacles in the way of the expansion of China. It is arguable that the defense links which have grown up between the Soviet Union and India redound to the advantage of the West, insofar as they strengthen Indian self-confidence vis-à-vis China and do not result in the exclusion of the West's own, still more substantial influence in the Indian subcontinent. The same may be true of the increase of Soviet influence in other countries in the Indian ocean area.

Moreover, we do not yet know what emphasis will be placed by the Soviet Union on the build-up of her capacity for global naval diplomacy and military intervention. Her lack of carriers is still a major handicap as far as invasion from the sea is concerned; and at present the Mediterranean, rather than the Indian Ocean, is where this new disturbance in the balance of naval power is being felt. Nevertheless the Soviet Union could within the next few years achieve a position in the Indian Ocean in which it could intervene in situations in many of the littoral states and become a major naval factor in the area. The technique has already been demonstrated by the influence of Soviet warships in the Mediterranean on relations between Israel and the Arab states.

China might have much to gain from an opportunity to exert naval power in the Indian Ocean, both in order to bring pressure to bear on India and Southeast Asia and so as to counter the activities of Soviet and U.S. submarines threatening her from the Bay of Bengal. China does not yet have any foothold in the Indian Ocean; nor does she yet have naval forces enough to make much use of one if she did. At present her submarine force can effectively operate only in the Pacific, apart from one G-class submarine. China does, however, have some prospect of gaining a foothold in Zanzibar; and it is possible that her relationship with Pakistan might bring her the use of Chittagong, or that use of Rangoon or Singapore might become available to her as the result of political changes in the area. Fear of Chinese naval collaboration with Pakistan appears to have played a part in the recent Indian decisions to place increased emphasis on the navy and divide it into Western and Eastern Commands, the former to be located at Bombay and the latter at a projected base at Visaka patnam.

POSSIBLE WESTERN RESPONSES

If the withdrawal of the British and the improbability of their return in significant strength does endanger Western interests in the Indian Ocean area what steps should be taken to meet the situation? If anyone is to succeed the British in their role in Southeast Asia and the Indian Ocean it will not be by establishing a physical foothold in the places Britain has vacated. It is clear that the United States does not propose to establish herself in Singapore, and that she would not be welcome there if she did. It is not yet clear what obligations Australia and New Zealand will assume toward Malaysia and Singapore as the result of the five power talks scheduled for May 1968, nor whether they will take the form of the continued presence of air, land and sea units there; but if they did, the Australian-New Zealand role would be less than, and different in character from, that which has been played by the former imperial tutor.

It would appear that only the United States is capable of intervening effectively in the areas vacated by Britain and of policing the Indian Ocean; and that to do so effectively she requires naval facilities in Western Australia. The United States does not at present keep substantial naval forces in the Indian Ocean area. She would be capable of sending units of the Seventh Fleet, but these at present have no base closer than Subic in the Philippines. She has sometimes sent units of the Sixth Fleet through Suez to exercise with allied navies in the Indian Ocean, but the canal is closed for the foreseeable future. As Dr. T. B. Millar has written: "The plain fact is that of all the countries [bordering the Indian Ocean] with facilities to offer, only Australia has the industrial backing needed to support them and the internal stability which would assure continuity of usage." [7]

The British withdrawal has made many Australians anxious about this country's Indian Ocean approaches. In 1965–1966 46 per cent Australian exports and 56 per cent imports crossed the ocean. Australia brings 60 per cent of her oil across the ocean from the Middle East.[8] The vast mineral extraction industry that is developing in northwest

[7] T. B. Millar, "Control of the Indian Ocean," *Survival,* October 1967.
[8] See T. B. Millar, *op. cit.*

Australia and transforming the country's export trade, will be a heavy user of ocean transport. Yet Australia's own growing naval forces are based in southeastern Australia and deployed chiefly in the Pacific. Consideration is now being given in Australia to the purchase of an attack carrier (the Royal Australian Navy's one carrier is used for ASW purposes) and to the construction of a naval base at Cockburn Sound in Western Australia. It has also been suggested that if Britain should lose interest in the British Indian Ocean Territory, Australia should seek to have sovereignty over these islands transferred to herself, at the risk of incurring the disapproval of India, who has been critical of the establishment of the Territory.

The United States already possesses an important naval communications station at North West Cape in Western Australia, part of the global communications network for the Polaris force. Under an Anglo-American agreement published in April 1967 she has the right to make use of the British Indian Ocean Territory. The Australian project of a naval base at Cockburn Sound was stimulated in part by a British interest which has now disappeared in stationing naval and amphibious forces in the area after withdrawal from Singapore. If this project is now pursued without the British, it may result in an important new facility available to both Australian and U.S. naval forces.

When the conflict in Vietnam is over, the United States and Australia will have to choose between continuing to maintain a physical foothold on the Asian mainland, and influencing Asian affairs from secure bases on the periphery. In the event that the latter course is chosen, Australia is likely to become once again, as it was during the Second World War, a major center of U.S. operations. But whichever choice is made the problem of policing the Indian Ocean will remain. The solution to this problem requires the stationing of U.S. naval forces in the Indian Ocean and the provision of naval facilities in Western Australia for use by the two countries.

Summary

Seapower in the Indian Ocean serves the purposes of United States policy first, by contributing to strategic nuclear war forces; second, by making possible military intervention in local Asian conflicts; and third, by serving as an instrument of diplomacy in a variety of ways that stop short of war or the specific threat of it. A basic presupposition of U.S. policy in Asia has been a British presence, including a naval presence, in Southeast Asia and the Indian Ocean. By the end of 1971 Britain will be not only without bases in the area, but also without substantial capability or will to intervene there from outside. New threats to the area may arise in the form of increased instability, and Soviet and Chinese activity in the area. Consideration should be given to the stationing of U.S. naval forces in the Indian Ocean and to the construction of naval facilities in Western Australia for use by the two countries.

Marshall D. Shulman

5

The Soviet Turn to the Sea*

Technology and politics have combined to turn the Russian outlook upward into outer space and outward across the seas. Traditionally, the awareness of the land, the vast and sprawling land, stretching from frozen arctic to tropical desert, astride Europe and Asia, has overhung the Russian consciousness, has shaped its history, defined its defenses, set the background for its culture and literature, and nurtured its spirit.

Now, in the middle of the twentieth century, quite suddenly as time is measured in history, the Soviet perspective has widened in many dimensions. It is outer space that first captures the imagination, that arouses the vision of a modern Soviet technology. But it is the turn to the sea, quieter and less dramatic, that may have the more profound consequences in determining the role of the Soviet Union as a great power in the coming decades.

In all its varied aspects—scientific, economic and military—the expansion of Soviet activities in relation to the seas stems from and is a function of a central political conception: that events have made oppor-

MARSHALL D. SHULMAN *is professor of government and director of the Russian Institute at Columbia University. He was special assistant to the Secretary of State from 1950 to 1953, associate director of the Russian Research Center at Harvard University from 1954 to 1962, and professor of international politics at the Fletcher School of Law and Diplomacy, Tufts University, from 1961 to 1967. He is the author of* Stalin's Foreign Policy Reappraised *and* Beyond the Cold War.

* Associated with Professor Shulman as research assistant in this project was Edward L. McGowan, a graduate student in the Department of Public Law and Government at Columbia University.

tune and necessary the widening of Soviet interests and operations over a world-wide theatre of action. This conception, in contrast to the continental perspective which had heretofore emphasized theatres of action peripheral to its borders, began to manifest itself in the thinking of the Soviet leadership in the early 1950's.

What were the events which led to this change in political perspective?

Among the technological developments whose implications began to shape this outlook were the changes in transportation and communications which brought all parts of the world within effective political reach; also of course the radical changes in weapons technology, which shifted the focus of Soviet strategic reliance upon a large land-army to airpower and missiles, and thereby to a balance of nuclear deterrence, which interposed a qualitative separation between local conflicts and general war. Illustrative of the many ramifications of the new weapons technology was the prospect of nuclear propulsion on and under the oceans, with its potentialities for a radical extension of maritime operations everywhere in the world, including the polar seas. (This is not to say that the Soviet leadership was the first to realize these implications in every case, or that the effects of these developments were immediately perceived, but that by the middle 1950's the implications had begun to shine through the bureaucratic thickets and to modify habitual modes of thought.)

On the political side, meanwhile, the relative stabilization of the Central European theatre of action contrasted with the political ferment elsewhere in the world resulting from the sudden dissolution of colonial relationships. The industrial areas of Europe remained important to Russia, but were by now susceptible at best to marginal changes, small in degree and long-term in political effect. In Asia, Africa and Latin America, on the other hand, opportunities for political action were becoming increasingly attractive. Moreover, the Soviet leadership perceived by the early 1950's that new configurations of political power were emerging, and that some among the new nationalist forces of the underdeveloped world might be drawn into a loose coalition against Western "imperialism." Possibly, the 1952 intervention of the Afro-Asian bloc into the diplomatic battles concerning a resolution of the Korean conflict may have dramatized this potentiality for the first time in the minds of the Soviet leadership. By 1953, the Soviet Union signalled its readiness to participate in technical assistance programs of the Economic and Social Council; by 1955 the Communist bloc began its military aid to Egypt and the Soviet leadership was travelling widely on voyages of rediscovery of the Third World; and at the landmark Twentieth Congress of the Communist Party of the Soviet Union in

1956, the leadership gave doctrinal sanction to a world-wide foreign policy. The significant point is that the new doctrinal guidelines signalled more than an enlargement of the geographical perspective; by its emphasis upon "peaceful coexistence" and "zone of peace," the Soviet leadership was marking the transition from a revolutionary policy to one appropriate to the Soviet Union as a great power operating in a context of competition between power-bloc coalitions.

Thus, the constraints imposed by the new weapons, the opportunities created by the dissolution of old empires, the relative stability of Europe, and the technical feasibility of operating in the destabilized areas across the oceans, all combined to encourage a broader geographical outlook on the part of Stalin's successors. Once this outlook was arrived at, certain imperatives in ocean policy followed. An enlargement of the merchant marine was needed to carry both trade and aid, without having to be as dependent upon foreign shipping. A modern navy was required, to protect shipping, to project the Soviet "presence" abroad, and to play its part in both strategic deterrence and local conflict situations (although, as we shall see, the full realization of this latter function was to become apparent only later). A modernized fishing industry was also necessary, for trade, for technical assistance, for foreign currency, and to support the domestic economy. An expansion of resources devoted to oceanographic research (in which interest was stimulated in the Soviet Union as elsewhere by the experience of the International Geophysical Year in 1957) was also required to give practical assistance to the navy, the merchant marine and the fishing industry. From this followed also increased attention to the development of ocean engineering, to support scientific research and the exploitation of the mineral resources of the ocean and the seabed, and the expansion of ocean services to protect shipping and the coasts with information regarding weather and ice conditions (of particular importance, for example, to the Northern Sea Route, which was now to acquire an enlarged role in connecting Europe and Asia).

Some Implications of Soviet Ocean Policy

From these beginnings of the Soviet expanded effort in various aspects of its ocean policy in the middle 1950's, the further unfolding of these programs began to take on a life of its own, as government activities tend to do anywhere, responding in piece-meal fashion as new needs began to appear. Through the 1960's, in successive stages, broader aspects of international politics have become involved, as these programs have interacted with external events. Soviet relations with the United States inevitably have been affected by, and have in turn had their effect upon, Soviet ocean activities. Internally, the way in which the Soviet system administers and seeks to coordinate programs of such a variegated nature has raised questions of comparison with the effort at coordination of similar programs on the part of the United States.

INTERNATIONAL POLITICAL ASPECTS

It is apparent upon reflection that various elements of Soviet ocean policy were involved in and deeply affected by such political developments of the 1960's as the deepening dispute with China, the Cuban missile crisis, the fall of Khrushchev, the conflicts in the Middle East, Vietnam and elsewhere, and the alternating moods of détente and intensified rivalry and military competition with the United States. What follows are suggestive illustrations of these interactions; some will be dealt with more systematically later, but many will remain as an agenda for future study.

If the Soviet Union has its adherents of Mackinder's geopolitical determinism, their reflections on the effect of the dispute with China upon the relative claims of the two countries to a "heartland" position are not recorded. In simpler terms, it seems likely that the actual or potential interdiction by China of Soviet rail routes to the Far East may have provided additional stimulus for the Soviet development of maritime capabilities, including the further improvement of the Northern Sea Route, and the offer in 1967 to open that route to foreign shipping. (Further illustrations of the interrelatedness of various aspects of ocean policy are suggested by the technological development of nuclear-powered ice-breakers, scientific advances in weather forecasting and navigational aids, and, on the political side, the closing of the Suez Canal—all of which contributed to the increased utility of the Northern Sea Route.)

The inter-relationship of political, economic and military purposes is also illustrated by the potential or actual utility of Soviet foreign aid programs in obtaining base rights strategically located near narrow straits (Suez, Gibraltar, Gulf of Aden), and port facilities useful for Soviet fishing trawlers (Cuba, Egypt). These trawlers produce a significant amount of foreign currency for the U.S.S.R. from sales of fish, and the currency in turn helps to finance Soviet aid programs. Other aid programs have been directly related to the development of shipping or naval facilities useful to the Soviet Union (Cuba, Egypt, Syria, Indonesia and in the Indian Ocean area).

In more direct military applications, the Soviet turn to the sea has opened up for debate in the Soviet Union as elsewhere questions concerning the role of modern seapower. The most interesting aspects of this debate concern the development of Soviet thinking about the role of the submarine as part of the nuclear deterrent, the possibility of limited wars at sea in the future, and the function of naval power in relation to local conflicts in remote areas. Questions which have been raised outside the Soviet Union largely concern varying estimates of the extent to which the expansion of Soviet naval capabilities reflects a more adventurous intention to enlarge Soviet influence by military means. In addition to the general questions that are raised affecting the competitive levels of the respective navies (for example, differences regarding the rate of output of Soviet nuclear submarines), there are special aspects which have excited particular concern, such as the possibility that the increased Soviet naval presence in the Mediterranean is part of an effort to achieve a positive Soviet sphere of influence in the Middle East, and the possibility that increased mobility of Soviet military forces may portend a lower threshold for intervention in local conflict situations which it may define as falling in the category of "national liberation struggles."

Finally, as part of this preliminary survey of some international political aspects raised by the expansion of Soviet ocean interests, a number of questions can be identified stemming from the development of Soviet positions in international law, in international organizations, and in regard to various forms of international cooperation. Soviet interests are obviously deeply engaged by current efforts to redefine the territorial sea, the continental shelf, and the meaning of freedom of the seas under contemporary conditions. In the United Nations, the Soviet Union has found itself obliged to make decisions regarding the useful functions of the General Assembly as against such bodies as the Economic and Social Council and UNESCO in matters concerning the sea, and to respond to the growing sentiment among smaller nations for the extension of United Nations sovereignty over the resources of the deep sea. In many aspects of international cooperation, including bilateral and multilateral fishing agreements, international conservation conventions, and in scientific cooperation in oceanography, the Soviet Union has become more deeply and constructively involved.

SOVIET AND U.S. SEA POLICY COMPARED

Three primary points should be kept in mind in comparing Soviet and American sea policies:

1. The Soviet initial thrust to the sea roughly parallels the expansion of similar U.S. activities in time, and quite naturally stemmed from many of the same technological and political considerations. In the case of the United States, which entered the post-war period with a very large naval capability, the awakening marked less of a directional turn, but the great expansion of U.S. interest in oceanography and in the

role of the Navy as part of a nuclear deterrent came in the late 1950's, and had another spurt of growth in the middle 1960's. The International Geophysical Year stimulated oceanographic interests in the United States as it did in the Soviet Union, and the development of undersea nuclear propulsion has aroused the American imagination at least as much as the Soviet, and considerably earlier.

2. Although the Soviet ocean program is sometimes represented as an effort to find a break-through to supremacy, in several important respects the Soviet program appears to be merely responsive to leads by the United States. For example, the development of nuclear-powered submarines and of mobile forces, including amphibious and naval infantry capabilities, both appear to have been responsive to comparable developments by the United States, and are as yet at lower levels of numbers and performance. The question is therefore still moot whether these capabilities are intended for offensive purposes, or to exercise an inhibiting influence upon American capabilities, which are perceived from Moscow as militant in intent. In certain other categories, however, the level of Soviet effort has clearly surpassed that of the United States, particularly in the fishing industry and in certain aspects of the merchant marine.

3. In the political uses of its ocean capabilities, the Soviet Union appears to be increasingly active in the sense that it is responding to opportunities presented by the recession of U.S., United Kingdom and to some extent French positions. In this regard, Soviet policy on the ocean is but one aspect of a general heightening of political rivalry in response to the decline of U.S. influence in Europe and elsewhere in the late 1960's.

THE ADMINISTRATION OF SOVIET OCEAN ACTIVITIES

Responding more or less at the same time and in roughly similar ways to the opportunities for intensified activities upon and under the world's oceans, the Soviet Union and the United States have developed and administered and sought to coordinate their efforts internally in ways that reflect the differences characteristic of their respective systems. To those who conceive of the Soviet system as giving highly centralized direction to all its activities in accordance with a master plan, the hundred or more semi-independent, loosely-coordinated agencies which operate in these fields may seem surprising. But there is such a diversity of ocean activities—ranging from oceanographic research (with more than 50 institutes) to ocean engineering, defense, fishing, merchant marine, foreign trade, mineral resources and foreign policy—that unified direction of these Soviet efforts would represent an impossible interference with a host of other administrative interests.

In an approximate sense, here as in other fields, the ultimate coordination and direction may be achieved in the higher organs of the Communist Party and their staffs, in the Praesidium of the Council of Ministers and insofar as it concerns the allocation of resources, in the State Committee for Economic Planning (GOSPLAN).

In the field of oceanography alone, by far the bulk of the research is conducted in institutes under the various ministries (both All-Union and Union Republic) and directorates with relevant interests: defense, fishing, shipping, hydrometeorology, geology, etc. Other research, including basic research (which is proportionately less strongly represented than in the United States) are conducted by institutes under the Academy of Sciences of the U.S.S.R., or the Academies of Sciences of the various Republics, or the universities under the Ministry of Higher Education. Coordination of this research is exercised by two bodies. One, whose responsibility mainly concerns basic research, is the Coordinating Committee for Oceanography under the Earth Sciences Department of the Academy of Sciences, U.S.S.R. This Committee brings together directors of research in the universities and in the institutes under the Academy. The other body, with a principal responsibility for applied research, is the Coordinating Council on Oceanography of the State Committee on Science and Technology, which operates directly under the Council of Ministers. This Council consists of representatives of the various ministries and some of the institutes involved in oceanography, including those institutes under the Academy of Sciences. Although this Council has served mainly as a coordinator of information and does not have control over research programs or budgets, it may in practice have considerable behind-the-scenes influence because of the prestige and political authority of the State Committee on Science and Technology.

It is difficult to say whether in practice the degree of coordination in the field of marine affairs is appreciably greater in the Soviet Union than in the United States. Since 1966, the Marine Sciences Council, under the chairmanship of the Vice President, appears to have exercised about the same degree of coordination of the activities of the 24 bureaus of 11 federal departments and agencies involved in this field as do the two Soviet bodies; in addition, it seeks together with an independent advisory commission to articulate national goals and priorities in marine science policy in a way that is not publicly done in the Soviet Union. But a major difference is in the large number of activities in the United States which are outside the government: private and university research institutes, commercial firms, including fishing and merchant marine, oil companies, engineering and shipbuilding firms—some of whose activities may be loosely coordinated in some degree by government contracts or subsidies, but may be even more affected in diverse directions by separate and private interests. The effect of this difference is less apparent in the field of oceanography or defense, however, than in such other branches of ocean policy as fishing and shipping.

Soviet Oceanography

SCALE OF SOVIET OCEANOGRAPHIC EFFORT

The most striking characteristic of Soviet oceanic research is the rapidity with which it has grown over the past fifteen years or so from almost a standing start to the point at which it is second only to, and in some respects approximately equal to that of the United States, having surpassed France, Japan and Britain, the other countries most active in this field.

Exact comparisons of numbers of oceanographers are difficult to make, because categories are not altogether comparable, but a rough comparison suggests that the oceanic research force is approximately equal in the Soviet Union and the United States. It was estimated in 1964 that Soviet oceanographers numbered between 1,200 and 1,500; in the United States, the figure for 1967 is given as slightly over 1,000 for oceanographers strictly defined; if such related categories as fisheries scientists, oceanographic engineers, technicians, etc., are added, the figure approaches 5,000. The Soviet work force also includes a high number of technicians supporting the oceanographic scientists; also, approximately 30 per cent of the work force in this field is made up of women.

Soviet expeditions and oceanographic research teams now cover the world's oceans. In terms of numbers of vessels, the Soviet oceanographic fleet is estimated at approximately 160, and is expected to approach 200 by 1970, a constant superiority over the United States of about 50 vessels for this period. As measured in size of research vessels, the Soviet oceanographic fleet passed that of the United States in mid-1964, now exceeds the U.S. fleet by approximately 50,000 tons, and is growing at a much more rapid rate.

A comparison of numbers of oceanographic research institutes is also not altogether representative of the relative efforts, in view of the qualitative differences between institutes and laboratories. As against the estimated 50 Soviet oceanographic research institutes, and an uncertain but much larger number of laboratories, there are in the United States more than 90 federal, 40 state, 90 academic and 25 private laboratories involved in some aspect of oceanographic research.

It was estimated in 1964 that approximately 60 Soviet oceanographers graduate annually from a five-year course of study at Moscow State University and several other university and institute training programs. This is roughly equivalent to a Bachelor of Science degree. The number of Soviet Ph.D.'s graduated annually in oceanography is not available, but in any case, a comparison with the United States would be inexact because of the numbers of trainees in biology, geology, etc., who work in related fields but may not be classified primarily as oceanographers.

Several hundred scientific books and monographs on oceanographic subjects have been published in the Soviet Union in recent years. Many of these are routine in character, and some consist of collections of articles which would tend to be published as journal articles in the United States. A number of journals in this field are published in the Soviet Union, bearing such titles as *Fishing Industry, The Maritime Journal,* and the general press frequently carries articles intended to educate the public on scientific aspects of ocean research and the great potentialities of marine resources.

QUALITY AND EMPHASIS OF SOVIET OCEANOGRAPHIC RESEARCH

It has already been observed that the primary emphasis in Soviet oceanography is upon applied research, and this is not surprising in view of the fact that most oceanographic institutes are under ministries or directorates having specific functional needs. The practical application of scientific knowledge is judged to be efficient. By far the greatest emphasis, apart from defense, is upon research in support of the fishing industry. Russian fishery science has a tradition which goes back to the eighteenth century, and it is now a world leader in this field. Most of the Soviet distant water research has been done to support the fishing industry, and is carried on under the Ministry of Fishing. The Soviet converted submarine, *Severyanka,* has been used, somewhat unsuccessfully, for fishery research, and a deep diving submarine, *Sever II,* has been under development primarily for research into fishing productivity.

In certain areas of basic research, however, American scientists have found Soviet work of high quality, particularly in marine biology and in work on the polar regions. Also, Soviet cartography is generally recognized to be of leading quality. In the routine collection and publication of data, Soviet performance is highly rated, although the World Data Center B in Moscow (the counterpart to World Data Center A in Washington), which was organized during the International Geophysical Year in 1957 to be an archival center for oceanographic information, has been found weak, perhaps because of a shortage of data-processing equipment. Soviet shore laboratories and ocean engineering capabilities have not been found impressive.

In breadth of interest and visionary prospects for the potential yield of research in a variety of directions, Soviet oceanography covers the full range reflected in U.S. work in this field, although differently distributed. There is extensive underwater drilling for oil and natural gas in the Caspian; modest experimentation in prolonged living under the waters of the Black Sea; sampling of the earth's core from the ocean floor; research on the extraction of sulfur gas from the Black Sea; some development of fish farming; research on harnessing energy from the tidal flow, and the extraction of heavy water from the ocean, among many other lines of activity and interests which have been publicly discussed. A leading academician delineated three basic directions for future oceanographic research as:

1. The physics of the sea, particularly the interaction of sea and ocean currents with atmospheric currents;
2. Comprehensive geological study of the ocean floor and shores; and
3. Ecology of all sea organisms, primarily of course, fish.

Among many other interests reflected in the Soviet general press are underwater seismic explorations, the purification of ocean water, problems of water pollution, studies of the floor of the Black Sea by amateur divers, contact with polar expeditions, and a great deal on the fishing industry and the living conditions of fishermen.

INTERNATIONAL ASPECTS OF SOVIET OCEANOGRAPHY

Much of the Soviet literature in this field is characterized by an international outlook, and emphasizes the importance of international scientific cooperation in this field. In the spring of 1966, the Soviet Union was host to the Second International Oceanographic Congress, sponsored by the Intergovernmental Oceanographic Commission of UNESCO. The occasion was an important one for opening up contact between Soviet scientists in this field and their foreign counterparts. More than 1,200 Soviet participants attended, and of the 700 or so foreign scientists who came, more than 200 were from the United States. The theme of the Congress was "Research on the Ocean for the Good of Mankind!" Articles in the Soviet press on the Congress and articles in Soviet journals on many other occasions stressed the notion that oceanographic research can only be done by cooperation among the scientists of various countries. Many U.S. scientists visited Soviet oceanographic institutes and laboratories after the Congress, and there have been active exchanges of scientists and scientific information between the two countries since that time.

Soviet scientists are thoroughly familiar with U.S. and other Western technical journals in this field, copies of which are duplicated in Moscow and distributed to all institutes and laboratories.

Oceanography has fitted into other Soviet foreign policy objectives in other ways. One aspect of the aid agreement between the Soviet Union and Indonesia of 1959 was the construction of an oceanographic research institute in Indonesia. A tangible result of the Soviet effort to cultivate common interests with France has been the Franco-Soviet mixed commission on economic, scientific and technical cooperation, at the third session of which, in January 1968, it was agreed that the two countries would conduct joint research expeditions on fishing resources in the Atlantic and Pacific oceans, and joint research on deep-sea marine resources in the Mediterranean.

A negative development from the Soviet point of view was the discontinuance by the Chinese People's Republic in the summer of 1967 of its adherence to a 1956 agreement with the Soviet Union and three other countries on cooperation in fishing and oceanography. China also declined to extend an expiring agreement on cooperation in aiding ships and aircraft in distress at sea.

Political Aspects of Soviet Military Capabilities at Sea

INDICATOR OF BELLIGERENT INTENTIONS?

To what extent should the large increase in Soviet naval capabilities since the end of World War II, and particularly in the last ten years, be taken as evidence of aggressive intentions? Much of the press treatment of the Soviet fleet and especially of the large number of Soviet submarines, estimated at from 360 to 410 in recent publications, has been alarmist in tone, implying an increased readiness on the part of the Soviet leadership to use force in extending Soviet power. In particular, the rate of increase in nuclear submarines is often advanced as posing a future strategic threat.

While no one can vouchsafe what may be the future intentions of the present or of future leaders of the Soviet Union, the nature of the increase in Soviet seapower suggests that the policy which animates the Soviet leadership as of now is less directed toward the use of these capabilities for military attack, than toward a more general expression of political power. What emerges from the assessment of technical specialists (cited in the bibliography at the end of this paper) is an impression that the kind of navy now being built by the Soviet Union might have considerable effectiveness in projecting the Soviet presence as a great power in many distant parts of the world, and may be a significant factor in reducing the relative authority of the United States to this degree, but it would not appear to be so constituted, or of such a magnitude, that it could expect to challenge American naval forces. This is of course a judgment about which there may be disagreement. The thrust of this assessment is not to denigrate the importance of Soviet naval capabilities, but to draw attention to the intangible and essentially political dimensions of power rather than to the simple scoreboard of war-fighting capabilities.

The nature of national power has become so variegated, so multidimensional, so much affected by intangible and psychological factors, that it has become increasingly difficult to correlate some aggregate index of power with specific levels and types of military capabilities. In the effort to exercise influence over the political behavior of other nations and people, what constitutes a "presence"? The appearance of a flagship in a foreign port may no longer carry the symbolic force it did before the age of airpower and missiles, but there is no doubt that there is still a residual impact upon a contested area to have a visitation from even a few Soviet naval vessels as a tangible expression of political will that may be entirely out of proportion to the military capabilities these vessels represent. This effect was evident during the summer war of 1967 in the Middle East.

That the Soviet Union wishes to acquire the attributes and prestige of a great power with world-wide interests; that it wishes to inhibit the United States from the untrammeled exercise of its will around the world; that it wishes to encourage the contraction of the American presence and the decline of American influence, and to increase its own influence where American power has receded—all of this seems evident, and an inevitable aspect of the heightened national rivalry which now prevails between the two great powers. It is against this background that Soviet naval capabilities, as one instrumentality which is being used in concert with economic and political policies, must primarily be evaluated.

Brezhnev's demand in April 1967 for the withdrawal of the U.S. Sixth Fleet from the Mediterranean coupled with economic and military assistance to Arab nations and the manipulation of Middle Eastern tensions, and with the establishment of a permanent Soviet naval presence in the Mediterranean, suggest the unfolding of a policy which has moved from the effort to deny the Middle East to the United States as a zone of influence to the positive establishment of a Soviet sphere of influence there. The actions illustrate the orchestration of naval and other instrumentalities of policy.

In four years, the Soviet naval presence in the Mediterranean has been built up from virtually nothing to a permanent force of more

than 35 ships, including guided-missile cruisers, destroyers, submarines
and support and electronic intelligence vessels. The Soviet Navy has
learned to refuel and resupply its ships at sea, as the American navy
has been doing. It has not so far established shore bases in the area,
but it has been operating out of Alexandria, Port Said and Latakia,
and has indicated its interest in the Algerian port of Mers-el-Kebir
after the departure of the French from that base, situated 350 miles
from the Straits of Gibraltar. The possibility of a strong naval position
astride the Suez Canal and the Straits of Gibraltar, combined with
strong political positions in the Middle East, offers many attractive
strategic advantages: a more secure southern flank, easier lines of communication to unstable areas in Africa, and potential wartime control
over the flow of resources to southern and southeastern Europe, although the absence of air cover raises questions about its effectiveness
under wartime conditions.

Whether this combination of circumstances can be duplicated elsewhere (for example, in the Indian Ocean) is still unclear, but in this
instance at least it is apparent that the augmented Soviet Navy has
played a vital role in supporting Soviet diplomatic objectives.

THE SOVIET NAVY AND "WARS OF NATIONAL LIBERATION"

The intensification of the war in Vietnam in early 1965 appears
to have had important effects upon the military policies of the Soviet
leadership which came to power shortly before. In addition to increases
in the military budget and measures to strengthen Soviet strategic
capabilities, the Brezhnev-Kosygin regime also sought to improve
Soviet capabilities for dealing with remote conflict situations. This
effort was to have important consequences for the Soviet Navy. It
meant the development of naval forces that could transport, supply
and offer combat support to conventional forces in distant local conflicts; it meant the development of amphibious landing ships, the reac-
tivation of the naval infantry, a small elite force trained for landing
operations, and the acquisition of some helicopter carriers.

In the political background were several relevant factors. The Vietnam conflict was seen, not as a unique phenomenon, but as an illustration of two political trends. One was the continuing political conflict
likely to characterize the turbulent aftermath of sudden de-coloniza-
tion, which would be likely to erupt in many other areas; the other
was, as perceived from Moscow, the militant imperialism of U.S.
policy, as reflected in the Dominican crisis, the Bay of Pigs, the
landings in Lebanon, and then Vietnam. A major theme that emerged
in Soviet political declarations was that "wars of national liberation"
were likely to be one of the main characteristics of the present period

of international politics. What was left unclear in these declarations was the extent to which the Soviet Union felt called upon to intervene in any local conflict situation which it defined as a "war of national liberation." In earlier instances, the Soviet Union had clearly felt inhibited, and perhaps frustrated, by its lack of capabilities for such intervention. Now that its capabilities were improving, therefore, did this bespeak an intention to pursue a policy of more active military intervention in future local conflict situations? Or did it essentially reflect an intention to inhibit the United States from intervening?

The latter possibility is suggested by two considerations. One is that the Soviet move in these directions appears to have been responsive to what it preceived as a U.S. lead. The other is that Soviet policy has generally been characterized by caution in the involvement of its own forces in conflict situations; it has carefully controlled the risks of becoming engaged in a way that would lead to an automatic commitment.

However, even if the initial Soviet intention is to inhibit "imperialist" intervention, it is of course possible in any actual situation, whatever intentions may have prevailed beforehand, for capabilities to beget their own intentions. Whether this will mean in practice a lower threshold for Soviet intervention in future local conflict situations may depend upon such external factors as the particular interests at stake in any specific conflict situation, and whether they primarily engage U.S. or Chinese interests, and in turn what policies the United States and China will follow in regard to future conflicts.

Economic Aspects of Soviet Ocean Policy

As in other aspects of its national life, the Soviet Union guides its economic activities connected with the ocean both from the point of view of their economic utility to the nation and as ancillary measures in support of political, diplomatic and military objectives. The merchant marine which carries Soviet goods in world trade also earns foreign currency, keeps the Cuban economy viable, bears military aid to the United Arab Republic and to North Vietnam, reduces Soviet dependence on foreign shipping, and carries the Soviet flag into the ports of the world. The Soviet fishing industry which adds proteins to the Soviet diet (compensating for deficiencies in Soviet agriculture) also earns foreign currency, is a useful element of technical assistance and foreign aid to a dozen or more underdeveloped countries, and supports research of indirect, but considerable, military significance. The oil reserves under the waters of the Caspian add greatly to Soviet political and economic leverage in both Eastern and Western Europe.

Therefore, although economic activities on the ocean may be dealt with separately for analytical purposes, in practice it is clear that they are of more than purely economic significance.

THE SOVIET MERCHANT MARINE

From the middle 1950's, and more emphatically after 1960, Soviet economic planners have been putting an increasing emphasis upon the modernization and enlargement of the Soviet merchant marine. By 1961, Khrushchev recorded a 50 per cent increase in tonnage over 1956. A growth of 150 per cent in capacity was claimed for the period 1958–1965, and the Five Year Plan directives published during the 1966 Party Congress emphasized the "construction of high-speed mechanized ships with a large cargo capacity" as well as the further development of ports and ship repair yards. For the year 1967, an increase of 18 per cent in cargo shipments and 8 per cent in cargo volume was claimed. As of 1967, the Soviet merchant fleet was estimated to number approximately 1,700 vessels with about 460 additional vessels under construction. The Soviet Union now ranks seventh among the maritime nations on a deadweight tonnage basis, and it is expanding at a rate of one million tons a year. Its merchant fleet is modern (half of its oceangoing vessels are five years old or younger), and the Soviet Union is now able to carry about half of its foreign trade in its own ships. The U.S. merchant fleet is larger in tonnage, but it has been declining in recent years.

In an effort to stimulate productivity and efficiency in merchant marine construction and operation, Soviet planners have brought the industry wholly under the new economic reforms in incentives and planning. A profit of 30 per cent was said to have been earned by maritime transport in 1967. Premier Kosygin has emphasized, and technical journals have amplified, the importance of wider application of electronic computers in controlling ship traffic, and the training of maritime personnel in the use of the computers. For the Soviet Union as for Japan, the widespread application of new technology in increasing speed and capacity of merchant shipping is steeply increasing their respective shares of the ever-larger volume of world shipping.

A major advantage to the Soviet Union is the availability of low-cost ship-building facilities in East Germany and Poland, which do not require the use of foreign exchange. Pressure by the Soviet Union upon the German Democratic Republic to sell merchant ships at 30 per cent below the prevailing world price level has been reported. At the Twenty-third Party Congress in 1966, it was stated that 48 per cent of the deliveries of new Soviet cargo ships through 1970 would come from other countries in the Soviet bloc. Soviet journals also speak of the construction of tankers in Leningrad shipyards for East European allies.

Ships and ship-building facilities have played an important part in Soviet and Soviet-bloc foreign aid and technical assistance programs to Indonesia, Algeria, and Egypt, among other countries; the Soviet merchant fleet has been heavily engaged in carrying an estimated million-dollar-a-day volume of cargo to Cuba, and there are indications that Soviet ships have had to be withdrawn from other service to maintain this volume.

Reference has already been made to the military as well as the economic importance of the Northern Sea Route, as a link between Murmansk and the Pacific. Early in 1967, the Soviet Minister of Merchant Marine, Viktor G. Bakaev, announced at a press conference that the Soviet Union would open the Northern Sea Route to foreign shipping, perhaps in the hope of attracting European and Japanese contributions toward the heavy costs of keeping this Arctic route clear. With the help of an atomic-powered icebreaker, it has been possible since 1959 to extend the season during which this route can be used beyond the previous three and a half months; modern navigational aids and improved weather forecasting have also helped to reduce the hazards of this route. Meanwhile, the closing of the Suez Canal added to the attractiveness of the route, which had its most successful season in 1967 since its opening in 1930. The military significance of the growth of the Soviet merchant fleet also arises from the ready adaptability of freighters and passenger ships to defense applications.

THE SOVIET FISHING INDUSTRY

While the capacity of the U.S. fishing fleet has remained almost static during the 25 years 1940–1965, the Soviet Union has developed a modern high seas fishing fleet which by 1975, unless there is a significant change in Soviet policy, will be substantially larger than that of any other maritime power. If the Soviet coastal fishing capability is included, the Soviet fishing fleet is already the largest, fastest-growing and most modern in the world. In volume of catch, it was fourth in the world in 1968, after Peru, Japan and China. The United States, whose catch has been declining, was sixth, having been overtaken in 1966 by Norway. If the Soviets implement their present plans, their fishing industry could by 1975 bring in about $100 million in foreign exchange a year as well as provide from 4 to 5 per cent of the daily protein requirements of their population.

The great expansion of Soviet ocean fishing began in the middle 1950's. Since then, successive five year plans have kept pressing for increases in the volume of fish catch. At the Twenty-second Party

Congress in 1961, Khrushchev reported an increase in the fish catch from 2.7 million tons in 1955 to an estimated 3.7 million tons in 1961. In the five year plan presented at the Twenty-third Congress in 1966, an increase was projected from 5.8 million tons in 1965 to a planned 8.5 to 9 million tons by 1970. For the year 1967, the plan called for an increase in fish catch of 8.6 per cent, and in output of fish food products, 12 per cent. In a report on the plan results for 1967, the fishing industry was said to have fulfilled its plan, showing an increase of 108 per cent over 1966. However, the report said that the plan for "some fish products" was not fulfilled, without further specification. At a session of the Twenty-third Party Congress, one official criticized "short-comings in shore facilities, cold storage capacities and in the enlargement of the refrigerated and transport fleet," as well as inadequate repair facilities.

The large increase in the Soviet fishing industry has been attributed to the following factors: a high investment rate (estimated at $4 billion for the 1946–65 period), the introduction of flotilla fishing where the trawlers are accompanied by freezing and processing vessels, the creation of a large marine research organization, and the expansion of operations into all the oceans of the world. The Soviet trend, like the Japanese, has been toward larger trawlers, some with freezing capabilities, and a large storage capacity. The Russians have built large fleets of fishing vessels that stay at sea for months, including factory ships that have complete processing facilities. In some cases, fleets are provisioned by transport ships, which return the frozen catch to home ports. The productivity of Soviet fishing vessels has been greatly increased by technological advances, from such equipment as power winches to radar, sonic and ultrasonic devices for locating fish. Travelling in large flotillas, often of 100 or more, Soviet fishing vessels are accompanied by scouting vessels, which assist the fishing captains with information intended to maximize their productivity. The post-war development of deep-freezing techniques has been an important factor in making the fishing of distant waters practicable. The Soviet Union has become the world leader in the marketing of frozen fish and fish products; it has sought to limit the production of dried, smoked and salted fish products and to increase the output of fresh, frozen and canned products. Soviet food store windows often feature large displays of canned fish, some of which is still imported.

Although fish is not yet cheap or, in desired varieties, plentiful in the Soviet Union, it has been estimated that fisheries provide about one-third of the annual total animal protein consumed, perhaps offsetting shortages in the supply of proteins from livestock and agriculture.

While the Soviet Union has experimented with a fish protein concentrate, it has not gone as far in this direction as has the United

States, which has begun, since the approval given to this product in 1967 by the Food and Agriculture Administration, to manufacture the concentrate and to help several countries to build plants for its manufacture.

The Soviet Union has greatly increased its output of fishmeal, which it uses for fertilizer and a feed for livestock. The increase in output is almost a hundredfold from 1948 to the planned production for 1970.

The Soviet Union has built a number of large whaling factory ships to operate in the Antarctic, but the decline in the whale catch in recent years has led it to convert some of these to other purposes, as other countries have also. Of 16 whale factory ships known to be operating in the Antarctic in 1968, four were believed to be Soviet, two Scandinavian, and the rest Japanese. Japan and the Soviet Union also began exploiting the whales in the North Pacific as Antarctic catches diminished. An effective international agreement for the conservation of whale stocks has eluded many years of negotiating effort, and the consequences of this failure are already disastrously apparent.

It has already been observed that the administration of the Soviet fishing industry and fishery research is highly centralized. Since 1965, when Khrushchev's successors reversed his policy of decentralizing certain aspects of economic administration, the U.S.S.R. Ministry of Fisheries has directly administered all fishery enterprises, except for fish pond culture and domestic lake and river fisheries, which are administered by the respective Republics. The federal Ministry also administers the large and highly advanced fishery research program, which is said to engage more than 2,000 scientists.

The Soviet fishery industry and its research institutions have played an important role in Soviet relations with underdeveloped countries. Training courses on fishery biology and technology have brought to the Soviet Union many participants from developing countries. Among the countries to whom the Soviet Union has offered large fishery development projects are Yemen, Tanzania, Ghana, Senegal, India, Indonesia, Ceylon, Sudan and Somalia. It has built fishing ports in Egypt and Cuba, and offered three freezer-trawlers to North Vietnam. The Soviet Union has a large and rapidly expanding trade in frozen fish with a number of countries in Africa. This trade, which is important for both economic and political reasons, represents an increasing function of the expanding Soviet fishing industry.

Aspects of International Relations

The expansion of Soviet ocean activities inevitably has been accompanied by developments in Soviet positions on the international law of the sea, on the role of international organizations in ocean af-

fairs, and on the balance to be struck between international cooperation and national rivalry.

SOVIET APPROACH TO INTERNATIONAL LAW OF THE SEA

The Soviet Union has generally sought to express its interests and
policies within an interpretation of international law, and as Soviet
activities in and on the sea have developed, Soviet legal scholars have
been increasingly active in interpreting the customary international law
of the sea, and those legal questions which are moving toward clarification and codification, in terms which accord with Soviet interest. As
might be expected, Soviet writing in this field is not free from ideological overtones, often characterizing questions at issue as representing
a conflict between "progressive" and "reactionary" trends, but as in
other fields of Soviet legal writing, the ideological component is more
or less prefatory, while the main body of the argument enters directly
into the mainstream of international legal discourse.

The growing body of Soviet legal scholarship covers the same issues
as are dealt with elsewhere: territorial waters, the continental shelf,
contiguous zones, internal waters and the high seas; however a few
issues have special application to the Soviet situation, as for example,
the immunity of state-owned vessels.

The Soviet Union has acceded to three of the four Geneva Conventions on the Law of the Sea adopted as a result of a conference of 86
states in 1958—those concerning the territorial sea and contiguous
zone, the high seas and the continental shelf. In the case of the first
two conventions, its acceptance was accompanied by reservations. The
fourth convention, concerning conservation of fishery resources, has
not yet been ratified by the Soviet Union and is not yet in effect.

The question of the width of the territorial sea is one which was left
unsettled at the 1958 Geneva conference and at a later conference in
1960, and it has remained a persistent issue in international law. The
United States has championed a three-mile limit for territorial waters,
but toward the end of 1966, it extended its fisheries jurisdiction to 12
miles. The two countries have a common interest, however, in a relatively narrow definition of territorial waters, as against the extension
by some Latin American countries of their claim over fishing jurisdiction to 200 miles. The Soviet Union has been involved in recurrent
episodes with several Latin American countries on this account. Also
at issue in the definition of jurisdiction over territorial waters is the
right of peaceful passage, which vitally affects Soviet interests in the
transit of its naval vessels through narrow straits controlling access to
its principal ports. There is, as might be expected, a considerable
volume of Soviet legal writing to establish its position in terms of

customary law. At the same time, Soviet lawyers have written indignantly about the alleged intrusion of foreign submarines upon Soviet territorial waters as a violation of Soviet sovereignty. The Soviet position has sought to reconcile complete sovereignty over a nation's territorial waters with the right of peaceful passage for non-military vessels, and by special agreement for military vessels.

In the matter of contiguous zones, an issue of difference between the Soviet Union and the United States, among other countries, has been the question whether a country should have the right, if it is not able to do this by international agreement, to declare unilaterally "conservation zones" extending beyond the limits of its territorial sea. This issue was not resolved in the Geneva discussions of 1958 and 1960, and the convention which deals with this matter has not gone into effect.

Questions concerning the continental shelf are likely to be of increasing concern to Soviet legal scholars as advancing technology makes the rich resources of the shallow seabed more available, particularly because the convention on the continental shelf leaves unresolved important issues regarding the outer limits of the continental shelf and the degree of sovereignty to be exercised over continental shelf waters. In February 1968, the Presidium of the Supreme Soviet of the U.S.S.R. implemented the 1958 Convention on the Continental Shelf by passing a decree defining the sovereign rights of the Soviet Union over its continental shelf, declaring the natural wealth of the shelf as state property, and declaring its exclusive right to erect structures for research, exploration and development of the resources of the shelf.

More deeply political are Soviet writings concerning the principle of freedom of the high seas, since they are heavily engaged in such matters as the U.S. Sixth Fleet in the Mediterranean, the Seventh Fleet in Taiwan Straits, and the role of the U.S. Navy in the waters around Cuba. Quite naturally, Soviet lawyers seek to contain the operations of the U.S. Navy by as broad an interpretation as possible of the doctrine of freedom of the seas.

Of special interest to Soviet lawyers is the argument that state-owned vessels are entitled to immunity, as distinguished from the Western position that state-owned vessels engaged in commercial operations should be treated not differently from privately-owned commercial vessels. Here the discussion merely transfers to the ocean environment an old issue for the Soviet Union: whether its trading organizations abroad, being appendages of the government, should be entitled to diplomatic treatment; no doubt in time the matter will be adjusted by practical accommodation on sea as on land.

These are but a sampling of some of the issues concerning the law of the sea which have been discussed in the Soviet International Law Annual, which reviews current books and journal articles in this field. It will be apparent in the following section that current discussions in the United Nations have raised a number of related problems, particularly concerning rights over the resources of the seabed.

SOVIET RELATIONS WITH INTERNATIONAL ORGANIZATIONS

The proposal that the United Nations should be given title to the resources of the deep seabed has been actively discussed in the General Assembly since it was advanced by the Commission to Study the Organization of the Peace in 1966. As originally advanced, the proposal would also prohibit military use of the seabed; it further contemplated that the exploitation of deep-sea marine resources under U.N. control would result in considerable financial advantages to the international organization. A resolution embodying these proposals in a draft treaty was put before the General Assembly by Malta in August 1967. In the meantime, the Secretary General has been authorized to conduct a study of the subject, and an ad hoc committee of 35 states was established to prepare a study on various aspects of the seabed beyond national jurisdiction for consideration by the Assembly.

The attitude of the Soviet Union toward this role of the General Assembly in ocean affairs has not been made explicit. At a Pugwash Conference during September, 1967, a highly-placed Soviet scientist, Academician V. A. Engelhardt, director of the Institute of Molecular Biology, joined with an American scientist, Alexander Rich, professor of biophysics at the Massachusetts Institute of Technology, in cosponsoring a proposal that the mineral resources at the bottom of the sea be used by the United Nations to generate funds for economic assistance to developing countries, along the lines of the Malta proposal. There has been no indication, however, that this represents the position of the Soviet government, which has generally been averse to such developments, and would seem to prefer other, and smaller, forums for discussing ocean policy. At the first meeting of the ad hoc committee on March 18, 1968, the Soviet representative proposed a declaration in principle that the military use of the sea and ocean floor "beyond the scope of action of national jurisdiction," be banned, and suggested that the matter be referred to the 18-Nation Disarmament Committee for further discussion.

In general, the Soviet Union seems to have a preference for the "smaller and more technically-competent Inter-Governmental Oceanographic Commission of UNESCO as a forum for international discussions on ocean affairs. In 1966, as was noted earlier, the Soviet Union was host to the Second International Congress of the IOC. In February, 1967, the Soviet delegate proposed at a meeting of the Bureau and Consultative Council of the IOC that it establish a working group to draft conventions to govern scientific ocean research and the exploration and exploitation of mineral resources of the sea. This working group was created in October 1967, and it appeared possible that part of the Soviet intention was to head off action by the General Assembly in the same direction.

In addition to the IOC, the Soviet Union has participated in the work of several other international organizations related to ocean affairs, particularly since it began to take a more active interest in the underdeveloped world in the middle 1950's. Since 1953 the Soviet Union has been active in some of the technical assistance programs of ECOSOC. In 1955 the Soviet Union became active in the International Council for the Exploration of the Seas, an organization which was founded in 1902. Although the Soviet Union is not a member of the Food and Agriculture Organization, it has been represented by an observer at meetings of the FAO's Committee on Fisheries in recent years, and it has indirectly supported the organization's work in this field. The FAO fisheries promotion project in India, for example, is among the projects supported by ruble funds supplied by the Soviet Union. (Rubinstein, *The Soviets in International Organizations*, p. 44)

OTHER FORMS OF INTERNATIONAL COOPERATION

In general, the outlook of Soviet marine scientists has been markedly international, and the record of Soviet bilateral and multilateral cooperation in this field is exceptionally good. There is ample testimony that this has also characterized U.S.-Soviet relations in this area.

According to one marine biologist:

> On the international scene United States and Soviet Russian fishery scientists meet regularly to deal with matters common to them both, such as the fish stocks in the western North Atlantic. They exchange research personnel and work on each other's vessels. Thus they get to know each other's special problems and some of the proposed solutions and they agree with one another more often than not.

The Second Annual Report of the U.S. Marine Sciences Council, published in 1968, a year in which international tensions impaired many other forms of international cooperation between the two countries, presented this favorable picture:

> During the past year cooperation with the Soviet Union and other countries has increased in oceanography and fishery research. Specifically, there have been exchange visits of oceanographers, reciprocal calls by large

oceanographic research vessels, and development of collaborative fishery research projects. A useful step in improving cooperation has been the adoption of a United States policy to reduce administrative delays in arranging for Soviet fishery research ships engaged in bilateral research programs to call at United States ports.

Disputes over fishery matters between the United States and the Soviet Union have arisen from time to time, and generally have been resolved after discussions. In one instance in 1966, for example, the Soviet Union agreed to refrain from salmon fishing off the coasts of Washington and Oregon, and also agreed to permit on-board inspection of its trawlers. In the fall of that year, Senator Warren G. Magnuson of Washington met with Soviet fishery officials in Moscow, and held out the prospect of increased East-West trade in return for more compatible Soviet fishery practices.

Like other countries, the Soviet Union has entered widely into international fishery agreements and conservation treaties whenever its own economic interests seemed to require it. On the whole, these international agreements have been remarkably free from political complications. Some conservation conventions have been successful (notably the Pacific Fur Seal Commission) and some have not (the International Commission on Whaling) but the record of the Soviet Union in these matters is not notably different from that of other countries with fishing interests.

FUTURE PROSPECTS: NATIONAL RIVALRY
OR INTERNATIONAL COLLABORATION?

It is apparent from the foregoing account that the further expansion of ocean activity by the Soviet Union, the United States and other nations may lead in some fields to intensified national rivalry and in others to further international cooperation. The balance between the two is not foreordained.

Even in fields where promising beginnings have been made in international cooperation, such as fisheries and conservation, a number of potential conflicts can be anticipated, such as in the eastern Pacific and the Bering Sea, where planning and enlightened self-interest could avert mutually disadvantageous competitive practices. More effective conservation agreements are clearly necessary if stocks of certain species are not to be depleted by the pressure of a mounting world population upon the fishing industry.

Continued technological advances within the foreseeable future will be likely to increase competitive pressures upon the exploitation of the resources of the seabed. Will the nations of the world, and particularly the two great powers, trample each other in staking out their claims, like homesteaders of the Old West in their land-rush into newly opened territories? Or will some new balance of power concept for ocean resources evolve to give some measure of stability to the international system until organizational structures become stronger?

The alternatives are most starkly posed in the military side of ocean activities. The naval rivalries of today will soon be transformed by technology into wholly new dimensions, whose effect it is difficult to foretell. The race between submarine and anti-submarine technology is providing a powerful stimulus to much of today's ocean research on the part of the two great powers. The emplacement of military installations upon the ocean floor will soon be feasible. There is urgent need for anticipatory thinking about the effects of such developments: whether they will increase or reduce the stability of the military confrontation between the nations of the world, whether they will add to or subtract from the precarious margins of security now prevailing. Conceivably underwater seismic and sensor installations could be made to contribute to the stabilization of land as well as ocean weapons systems.

Finally, there is the as yet unrealized common interest of the nations in preventing the further contamination of the oceans, along with the rest of man's natural environment. If such common interests as these can be translated into common efforts, the sea can be a source of endless bounty and a calming factor upon national rivalries; if not, it will become a new dimension for despoliation and self-destruction.

Bibliographic Note

Material in this chapter was drawn from the following sources, among others:

Bardach, John, *Harvest of the Sea*. New York: Harper & Row, Publishers, 1967.

Burke, William T., "Legal Aspects of Ocean Exploitation—Status and Outlook," *Exploiting the Oceans*, Transactions, 2nd Annual Conference, Marine Technology Society, Washington, D.C., 1966.

———, *Ocean Sciences, Technology and the Future International Law of the Sea*. Columbus: Ohio State University Press, 1966.

Craven, John P., "Seapower and the Seabed," *U.S. Naval Institute Proceedings*, 92, No. 4 (April 1966), 36–51.

Dietz, Robert S., *Soviet Oceanography 1964: A Trip Report*. Washington, D.C.: U.S. Department of Commerce, 1965.

Effective Use of the Sea, Report of the Panel on Oceanography, President's Science Advisory Committee, Washington, 1966.

Goldman, Marshall I., *Soviet Foreign Aid*. New York: Frederick A. Praeger, Inc., 1967.

Keith, Congr. Hastings, "Fisheries Activities of the USSR," *Encyclopedia of Marine Resources* (forthcoming).

Laforest, Capt. T. J., "Strategic Significance of the Northern Sea Route," *USNIP*. 93, No. 12 (December 1967), 57–65.

Manheim, Frank T., "Soviet Books in Oceanography," *Science*. 154, No. 48 (November 25, 1966), 995–98.

Martin, Laurence W., *The Sea in Modern Strategy*. New York: Frederick A. Praeger, Inc., 1967.

Mathisen, Ole A., and Donald E. Bevan, "Some International Aspects of Soviet Fisheries." (A paper issued by the College of Fisheries) Olympia: State University of Washington, 1967.

Marine Science Affairs—A Year of Plans and Progress. (Second Annual Report of the U.S. Marine Resources Council) Washington, 1968.

Oswald, James W., "Toward a Political Theory of the Ocean," *Exploiting the Oceans*, Transactions, 2nd Annual Conference, Marine Technology Society, Washington, D.C., 1966.

Radio Liberty Research Bulletin, April 3, August 18, and December 6, 1967.

Rubinstein, Alvin Z., *The Soviets in International Organizations*. Princeton: Princeton University Press, 1964.

The Soviet Merchant Marine. Washington, D.C.: U.S. Department of Commerce, Maritime Administration, 1967.

Taracusio, Timothy A., *The Soviet Union in International Law*. New York: MacMillan, 1935.

Treadwell, Capt. T. K., Jr., "Soviet Oceanography Today," *USNIP*, 91, No. 5 (May 1965), 26–37.

Wolfe, Thomas W., "Russia's Forces Go Mobile," *Interplay*, 1, No. 8 (March 1968), 28, 33–37.

——, "Soviet Military Policy," *Current History*, 53, No. 315 (October 1967), 208–16.

Gordon J. F. MacDonald

6

An American Strategy for the Oceans

The development of a strategy for the oceans involves far more than an analysis of naval forces and how these forces could be applied in support of the national interest. Technical, political, and economic considerations are all of importance to U.S. policy for the oceans. The difficulty in this subject lies in understanding the relations between new technical achievements, the changing international situation, and the political climate in the United States and abroad; and the dependence of economic interests on all these factors.

In the decade of the 1970's, the United States will be presented with many opportunities in the oceans that can contribute to its national well being. In part these opportunities will be of the kind that have in the past provided for growth of the economy of the United States since possibilities for trade and investment abroad in countries bordered by the sea continue to grow at an increasing rate. Beyond the conventional uses of the oceans, advances in technology provide economic opportunities in further developing the resources of the sea, as well as using the sea in new ways for military purposes. These developments suggest that the sea will become a resource of greater importance than ever before and therefore a source of both power and dispute. The

GORDON J. F. MACDONALD *is vice chancellor for research and graduate affairs at the University of California, Santa Barbara. A former professor of geophysics and chairman of the Department of Planetary and Space Science at the University of California, Berkeley, Dr. MacDonald has also served as executive vice president of the Institute for Defense Analyses. He is a member of various scientific groups, including the President's Science Advisory Committee and the Defense Science Board. Dr. MacDonald is co-author (with Walter Munk) of* Rotation of the Earth.

opportunities for the United States in the oceans may be endangered by political developments restricting the use of the seas. These restrictions could arise from either unilateral acts of nations controlling strategically favorable portions of the oceans or from international agreements arrived at prior to an adequate technological, political, or economic assessment of the implications of such actions. A view of the ocean thus requires not only an analysis of the economic opportunities but also an appraisal of the developing relationships and interest of the sea-bordering nations of the world.

Economic Opportunities in the Oceans

OVERSEAS TRADE

U.S. economic interests in the oceans are dominated by the fact that a major portion of U.S. foreign trade is carried by ships. In 1966, the value of U.S. foreign trade was about $56 billion and over three-fourths of the goods were transported by ship. The ratio of total trade to gross national product stood at about 8 per cent in 1966; whether there will be a major shift in the 1970's depends on complex technological and political considerations but it seems unlikely. The situation in the Soviet Union stands in sharp contrast; it is estimated that the ratio of total trade to gross national product was about 5 per cent in 1966, the majority of which was with neighboring East European countries, with only 2 per cent of the gross national product actually involved in commerce overseas.

Although the U.S. merchant fleet is second in carrying capacity only to that of the United Kingdom, a substantial proportion of the U.S. foreign trade is carried either by ships under foreign flags or by ships that essentially fly an international flag (*e.g.,* Liberian vessels). While the merchant fleets of other countries, particularly the Soviet Union and Japan, grew rapidly in the 1960's that of the United States grew older and less well equipped to compete.

Several technological developments will influence the shape of merchant fleets of the 1970's. The development of surface effect ships capable of traveling at 100 knots in rough waters will provide economic competition to air cargo for high value freight. However, economic projections do not indicate that even large surface effect ships (about 5,000 tons or even greater) would be competitive with the conventional ships for bulk cargoes. The total market for goods requiring short delivery times, such as oranges and other perishable items, is only a minute fraction of the total U.S. trade abroad, so that for the civilian economy, surface effect ships will be of only minor importance.

A major deterrent to U.S. merchant marine activities in the 1960's was the high labor cost involved in maintaining ships at sea. Advances in automation could provide for far more economical operations. The United States is superbly equipped in a technical sense to lead in such developments since the automation of ships would depend on computers, navigational aids and similar equipments that have been produced in great quantities for missile defense forces.

A third major technological advance affecting foreign trade is the possibility of constructing very large ships which provide transportation on a very much lower ton per mile basis. One hundred thousand ton tankers were developed in the 1960's and one half million ton cargo vessels can certainly be constructed. The employment of such large vessels requires deep harbor facilities. In many areas, present harbors could not be modified by simple dredging but could be made capable of handling giant ships by extension outward using massive platforms with the buoyant elements extending well below the zone of wave action.

Japan took the leadership in the construction of the giant tankers in the 1960's. The reasons for the great Japanese success in building a modern merchant marine as well as selling giant tankers to other nations are complex, but one feature is worth noting as it illustrates the substantial problem for the United States if it is to develop a competitive shipbuilding industry. The Japanese shipyards are located in deep water ports and are close by the steel mills which to a very large extent are fed by water-transported iron ore. Very little of what goes into a Japanese ship travels by land over any distance. As a result the cost of the material, particularly steel plate, is substantially reduced over what it would be if it had been shipped from one end of the country to the other. The situation is vastly different in the United States. The major shipyards are separated by long distances from the steel mills and the high cost of rail transportation adds greatly to the cost of shipbuilding.

The development of a U.S. shipbuilding industry competitive with such countries as Sweden and Japan requires far more than modernization of shipyards, standardization of building practices, institution of automation and a reform of labor policies. It requires a determination of how the shipbuilding industry is to be integrated with other large industries so that proper advantage can be taken of such factors as geography and the lower cost of water transportation.

COMPARISON OF SOVIET AND U.S. OVERSEAS TRADE INTERESTS

The overseas interests of the United States and the Soviet Union differ greatly. The U.S. interest consists of the ownership of mines, oil fields, estates, factories, trading centers, as well as access to foreign owned sources of raw material and manufactured goods. Further, the dependence of the United States on overseas trade is substantially greater than that of the Soviet Union; the ratio of ship-carried trade to the GNP in the United States is three times that of the Soviet Union. U.S. foreign trade is highly diversified with the total trade amounting to over a billion dollars a year with two South American countries (Brazil and Venezuela), six western European countries (West Germany, France, Belgium, Italy, the Netherlands, and the United Kingdom), and two Asian countries (India and Japan).

The traditional Soviet policy of providing for itself a self-sufficient industrial base led both to relatively limited foreign trade and even more limited ownership abroad. However in the 1960's, the Soviet Union moved away from its position of virtual economic isolation. Two developments probably prompted this move. First, there was widespread recognition in the Soviet Union that the technology available in the western world might accelerate the growth of its own industrial base. Second, it was believed that foreign trade could be used as a means of entry into lesser developed countries which might then be politically exploited.

During 1960–1965, Soviet foreign trade turnover (imports plus exports) showed an annual growth rate of about 8 per cent reaching some $16 billion in 1965. Of this, $11 billion was in trade with Communist countries and $5 billion with the Free World. Of the Free World trade about $3 billion was with developed nations, principally in western Europe, and $2 billion with the lesser developed countries. Assuming a 6 per cent rate of growth by 1975, the total foreign trade turnover for the Soviet Union would be about $9 billion.

The Communist countries of Eastern Europe are the U.S.S.R.'s principal trading partners and account for nearly 60 per cent of Soviet foreign trade. Outside of Europe, Cuba is the largest Soviet customer with this trade consisting mainly of an exchange of Soviet manufactured goods and petroleum for Cuban sugar. In a sense this trade is economic aid for Cuba since the Soviets have a limited need for Cuban sugar. Soviet trade with the Free World's lesser developed countries consists primarily of exports from the U.S.S.R., about 10 per cent of Soviet foreign trade in the 1960's was with the lesser developed countries, while the U.S.S.R. accounted for less than 2 per cent of the total commerce of these countries. Although the Soviet Union maintains trading relationships with many of the lesser developed countries, about two-thirds of its exports have been concentrated in five countries: India, the United Arab Republic, Indonesia, Iraq and Afghanistan. Except for the buildup of the United Arab Republic's military goods following the UAR defeat by Israel in 1967, civilian goods rather than military goods made up the majority of the trade as measured in monetary terms.

ECONOMICS OF OCEAN RESOURCES

Although in the 1970's commerce overseas for both the United States and the Soviet Union will dominate their economic view of the oceans, the United States will also have a major economic concern with goods from the sea. There are opportunities for industrial exploitation in the four general areas of minerals, gas and oil; food from the sea; pollution control; and construction in the surf and beach zones. It is in these areas that possibilities exist for rapid change since these industries are so highly dependent on technology. Significant changes, however, depend upon the willingness of industry to engage in entrepreneurial activity, which in turn depends upon the resolution of a range of uncertainties clouding future investment prospects. These uncertainties in 1968 arose from five specific problems with regard to the oceans:

1. The uncertain legal status;
2. The character of the ocean environment and the technical difficulties of working within this environment;
3. The variability of the environment and the difficulties of accurately predicting the environment;
4. The difficulties in making economic predictions as to the return on investment;
5. Uncertain governmental programs.

Finally there were broad uncertainties about the future strategic posture of the United States with respect to the oceans. Strategic considerations are the major concern of this chapter; most of the listed areas of uncertainty have been treated in preceding chapters. I do, however, wish to add some additional thoughts, particularly with respect to technological restraints, predictive difficulties as to environment and return on investment, and uncertainty about the role of government.

Much publicity has been given to experimental dives of vehicles to the deepest parts of the ocean. These exploratory experimental dives give a deceptively encouraging picture of the ease of operation at great depths in the ocean. Long, reliable operations in the depths for commercial or military purposes are very different and more difficult than a quick penetration to the ocean bottom. For example, it was only in 1967 that a tethered buoy with attached instruments operated for as long as a year, and only in the same time frame that observations on the ocean bottom were conducted for as long as a few months. Major problems result from the fact that operations at great depths must be conducted at high pressures in an electrically conducting medium where communications are difficult and where there are severe limitations on visibility and sensing. A few examples suggest why industry is concerned about technological restraints to ocean resource development.

An important unresolved problem is the design of machinery which can operate reliably for long periods in free flooded conditions under high ambient pressure. No machinery component is literally free flooding. For example, an electrical cable contains gas at atmospheric pressure in the interstices between its wires. Under pressure at great depths this gas will often be squeezed into pockets and upon return to the surface will cause a bulge in the cable. Subsequent use of the cable can lead to a failure in the system depending on the cable. Similarly, gas inevitably found in cracks and interstices between metallic components is likely to be concentrated. One effect is that the gas includes hydrogen which can cause localized hydrogen embrittlement of the metallic parts. Thus, both theory and experience leads us to expect increased stressed corrosion in metals exposed to deep ocean pressures.

Different materials are also compressed by different amounts under pressure. This leads to high localized stresses, to separation of joints and laminations, and other difficulties, whenever dissimilar materials are in juxtaposition.

Quite apart from the effects of high pressure, free flooding equipment is immersed in a conductive medium. This obviously calls for proper grounding of dissimilar materials and for careful attention to the possibility of electrolysis. The exact forms of the electrical fields surrounding such equipment depends upon the location of electrical sources, electrical grounding, and all too frequently on electrical malfunction. There is a constant possibility of uncompensated fields resulting in rapid electrolytic corrosion.

The ocean is a most difficult communication media. The electromagnetic spectrum, except for the very lowest frequencies, is not usable under water. Communication must be either by hard line or by the use of sound. Reliance on acoustic transmission limits the velocity of propagation and the frequency to a few thousands of cycle per second. Not much information can be transmitted and what is transmitted may be badly distorted by the sea water. A related problem is that of visibility in sensing, since at depths, even with strong light sources, visibility can be restricted to a few feet by turbidity and the associated back reflection of the light.

The technical difficulties of operating in the ocean environment require that major efforts be devoted to the development of new materials, instruments, and tools for working within the ocean. All of these will demand substantial investment and experience of working in the ocean. A major policy question that emerges from such consideration is: Is there sufficient economic motivation in industries other than those in gas and oil to secure this experience without government subsidy? To what extent is the depletion allowance available to the oil industry a form of subsidy that has permitted substantial investments in technology? Is it appropriate that this experience be gained primarily in defense-oriented activities, with the information eventually being channeled into the support of the commercial exploitation of the oceans? Or are there other mechanisms by which industry can be encouraged to make the requisite investment?

The oceans present not only a difficult environment in which to work but also an unpredictable one. The petroleum industry in its off-shore drilling operations identifies as one of its major problems the forecasting of local and short term storms such as squalls that affect the profitability of drilling operations. For example, in the 1960's disasters in the Gulf of Mexico and the North Sea adversely affected insurance rates. Lloyds of London in 1966 doubled its insurance premium on big oil rigs to 10 per cent of the liability because in the span of six months storms sent five of eighty rigs insured by Lloyds to the bottom. Such problems, along with markedly high operating costs, decrease the profitability of off-shore operations.

Ability to work within the oceans to develop whatever resources may be there depends in a major way on describing and predicting the environment. Indeed exploration for mineral resources on the continental shelf as well as military operations requires the ability to work not only on the ocean bottom but throughout the water column above as well. Prediction of sea bottom conditions and conditions in the water column are as important to those operating in the oceans as prediction of weather and wave heights on the surface. Capabilities in these fields are severely limited and the state of the subject is one in which much basic research has to be done before adequate forecasting capabilities are achieved. Once these capabilities are achieved, there remains the problem of supplying forecasting service to the users.

On land, weather prediction services and storm warnings are provided by the federal government. These services are sometimes augmented by use of commercial operations, where industry has special needs not provided by governmental programs. The policy question of significance is whether the pattern of activity appropriate to the terrestrial environment is adequate for the much higher risk investments of the oceans. Should the government consider the provision of special services?

The difficulty in making meaningful economic analyses is a further barrier to large scale investment in the oceans. Development of the off-shore oil and gas industry provides a good example where such economic analysis was possible. Development of the off-shore deposits required only an extension of methods already existing of geologic and geophysical exploration. Drilling operations in the relatively shallow waters also represented an extension of existing capabilities and the cost of these extensions could be estimated with some degree of accuracy. Largely unforeseen were problems raised by the variability of the environment, and as a consequence labor and insurance costs were higher but these comprise a fraction of the total cost. Further, the relatively stable pricing structure in the oil industry permitted a detailed computation of the benefits which would arise from an exploitation of the off-shore resources.

The harvesting of manganese nodules provides an example where data and perhaps even methodologies are not available to permit a meaningful economic analysis. New methods of systematic geologic exploration have to be developed so that the resource areas can be accurately described. Techniques have to be developed for the harvesting of nodules and then the extractive technology developed for securing base metals from the complex silicate matrix. Information is just not available to permit an accurate costing of such a research and development program. There then follow the uncertainties with regard to the legal ownership of the materials of the deep ocean floor. Finally, there is the general question as to whether or not capital applied to the development of lower grade terrestrial deposits might not in the end lead to a more profitable enterprise.

A further uncertainty—indicated in Professor Skolnikoff's chapter—is the lack of an accepted pattern for the future organization of the federal government in ocean matters. This uncertainty handicaps industry in its planning and decisions. Even assuming the establishment of a new coordinating agency, industry will still have important questions as to the agency's range of functions. Would such an agency, which would fall considerably short of a "wet NASA," be adequately designed to supply financial, legal, regulatory, enforcement and advisory institutions as well as necessary services relating to the description and prediction of the marine environment? Supposing the establishment of a "wet NASA," the government will have to make substantial investments of its own for the development of ocean resources. In either case, questions critical to industry must be answered.

An illustration of industry's uncertainty with respect to government involvement is the case of fish protein concentrate (FPC). This is a substance resulting from concentration of protein available in whole fish which would otherwise not be suitable for human consumption. The technology required to produce fish protein concentrate had been available to the industry for several years in the 1960's. The government could have undertaken a major effort of exporting FPC or exporting the technology used to develop FPC. In the former case, it would have been a substantial opportunity for the American food industry to develop a product suitable for distribution, but in the latter case local food industries would be expected to make application of the U.S.-developed technology.

In addition to the role of government in support of ocean-going industry, there are important and related questions concerning the government's view of its strategy for the seas. To what extent is the government willing to protect U.S. investment in undersea resource exploitations abroad? This policy is critical because of the high initial investments required and the great vulnerability of many underwater operations to sabotage or disruption. It is most unlikely that American industry will place heavy investment even in potentially very rewarding but politically unstable regimes if there is no government assurance regarding the protection of such investments.

Strategic Considerations

RECENT EVOLUTION OF STRATEGIC POSTURES

The growth of U.S. trade investments abroad and the harvesting of U.S. ocean resources living and non-living, will depend to a considerable extent on how the United States uses its military forces, particularly naval forces, to contribute to national security and world peace. The strategic military view of the oceans has evolved substantially since World War II. In order to understand this evolution, it is useful first to review briefly recent developments in American and Soviet military strategy and to comment on possible Chinese interests.

The principal goal in American policy in the years immediately following World War II was to halt the spread of Soviet Communism, which threatened at that time to engulf all of Europe. During this time, neither the Soviet Union nor the United States concerned itself to any great degree with the Third World. The U.S. policy of deterrence which developed during these years centered about the possibility of using nuclear weapons against the Soviet Union, in support of a general war. Nuclear weapons delivered by aircraft were thought of as

additional bombs in the nation's total arsenal but not of such importance as to change the whole character of general policy. Since at this
time, the Soviet Union could not strike America's homeland, it relied
upon a very large land army as its deterrent to possible aggressive
moves on the Soviet Union or its allies by the Western powers. Planning
for naval forces on both sides was dominated by the thought of a land
war in Europe. The Soviet Union began to build up its submarine
fleet with the goal of providing a capability to interdict men and ma-
teriel crossing the ocean. Thinking in the American Navy was much
influenced by the experiences in World War II; there resulted an
emphasis on anti-submarine measures and a maintenance of a conventional surface fleet.

The takeover of China and then the Korean War were the first decisive moves which indicated that communist expansion threatened
not only Europe but a much larger part of the world. The use of the
U.S. Navy during the Korean War was largely conventional: guarding
major transport lines, providing fire support against coastal installations, and serving as a base for aircraft attacking both inland and
coastal targets. The highly successful Inchon landing was designed
along the lines of the South Sea Island operations of World War II and
again demonstrated the value of an amphibious attack force.

The development of fusion weapons in 1954, coupled with the supposed global threat of the communist bloc, led to new directions in
American strategy. Emphasis was placed on air power and the ability
to strike strategically the heartland of the enemy with a variety of
weapons. These were the days when the talk was of "massive retaliation," despite early warnings by critics that such massive retaliation
would be ineffective in deterring local conflicts. The Navy's role in this
strategy was the provision of large aircraft carriers from which bombers
could be launched to deliver nuclear weapons to the enemy's homeland. In response, the Soviet Union began to develop some capability
for attacking the United States with a small strategic bombing force.
The Soviet strategic nuclear capability, though growing, was small in
comparison with that of the United States; apparently Soviet force
planners believed that a small nuclear deterrent was sufficient. The
Soviet navy, however, did not have a role in nuclear deterrence but
continued to develop as a support for the Soviet army in a protracted
land war. The Soviets still relied heavily on a large land force as a
deterrent and as a protector of their European interests.

The launching of Sputnik I in 1957 focused public attention on the
fact that missiles rather than airplanes could be used to deliver nuclear
weapons. At the time, both the United States and the Soviet Union had
underway substantial programs for the development of intercon-

tinental ballistic missiles. Considerations both of geography and security for the offensive striking force led the United States to develop two quite different basing schemes: a land-based silo system and submarine-based nuclear missiles. The Soviets at first concentrated on land-based systems, since their much larger geographical area provided for a more widely dispersed system than was possible in the United States. Only later did the Soviets develop missile-armed submarines. As the two great powers built up their strategic strike forces they continued to focus attention on each other, although the Lebanon incident in 1958 again raised the question of the U.S. capability for conducting a limited war at great overseas distances.

Breakthroughs in technology shaped defense strategies in the early 1960's. Improvements in missiles made it possible for the United States to manufacture in large numbers sophisticated missile systems with great accuracy and low megatonnage, such as Minuteman and the Polaris submarine-launched system. A further development was that of reconnaissance satellites which permitted both the United States and the Soviet Union to obtain information with regard to either side's land-based strategic forces.

During the 1960's, the world's attention was increasingly drawn away from the competition of the two super powers. The break between the Soviets and Chinese made clear that the world could no longer be thought of in terms of two power blocs with a passive Third World. Instead, the development of a large number of crises, including those in Laos, the Dominican Republic, Cuba, and the Congo, together with the problems between Indonesia and Malaysia and finally the conflict in Vietnam, showed that the United States did not possess a deterrent to limited war. These events also made clear that the Navy had a far more complex role than that of providing a base for strategic strikes or guarding trans-Atlantic convoys.

Communist China, while on the whole following a belligerent foreign policy, such as undertaking campaigns to restore lost territory (for example, Tibet), spent relatively less on defense during the decade 1955–65 than the two super powers. China was striving to produce a nuclear force which would presumably act as a deterrent to U.S. ambitions in Asia by threatening Asian cities. Historically, China has not had a strong navy. The strategic role of the Chinese navy is not at all clear, though there have been reports of one or two Chinese "G" class conventionally powered missile submarines. Indeed, it would appear unlikely that China would develop a submarine-based nuclear force. Many large Asian cities are within intermediate range from Chinese borders so that a deterrent would not require even the development of an intercontinental missile. A submarine force is much more expen-

sive than a land-based force capable of delivering the same megatonnage. Geography is such that a Chinese submarine force would be
virtually useless against the Soviet Union.

Chinese interest overseas remained limited in the 1960's. Incident to
the break with the Soviet Union, China's trade policy shifted greatly.
By 1965, trade with the Soviet Union was limited to a few imports of
machinery and exports of textiles and ores. From the Free World, principally Japan and Canada, China imported grain and raw materials
as well as complete industrial installations and machinery. China
developed trade with Japan, and to a much smaller extent, with the
lesser developed countries, principally in Africa.

While it is important to China to establish itself as a major world
and nuclear power, China's long term policy will in all probability
have limited overseas objectives. Concern will be focused first on economic development and industrialization. Further, it may be expected
that China will compete with Japan for Asian leadership or at least
recognition by all Asian countries of China's dominance. In order to
accomplish this, China will wish to destroy the Republic of China and
eliminate American bases in Asia. The accomplishment of these goals
will not require a strong naval force but rather well-equipped land
forces backed by a nuclear deterrent. Because of this it is most unlikely
that China will develop as a major naval power in the 1970's.

OVERSEAS TREATY COMMITMENTS

Defense agreements in force in 1968 clearly illustrated the asym-
metry between the Soviet Union and the United States in their overseas strategic posture. In 1968, the Soviet Union was committed to the
defense of North Korea, Mongolia, Finland, and the Chinese Peoples
Republic through bilateral defense agreements and the Warsaw Pact,
and was aligned by further bilateral agreements with Czechoslovakia,
Poland, Romania, Hungary, Bulgaria, Albania, and East Germany. Of
the eleven countries maintaining defense agreements with the U.S.S.R.,
only Bulgaria, Albania, and East Germany do not border on the Soviet
Union, and only Albania does not border on another member of the
Warsaw Pact.

In contrast, the United States is the center of a network of multilateral and bilateral relationships involving some 42 countries. In
addition to the multilateral agreements, including NATO, SEATO,
ANZUS, and OAS, the United States had bilateral relations with
Japan, South Korea, Taiwan, and the Philippines. With the exception
of Canada and Mexico, all 42 countries which the United States is
committed to defend lie overseas.

A significant question for the 1970's is whether the Soviet Union with its increasing interest in foreign trade will develop defense agreements with countries overseas. Since it appears that a central objective of the Brezhnev-Kosygin regime was a reestablishment of credibility in Soviet political, economic, and military capability, the establishment of defense pacts with overseas countries would follow only on the development of Soviet capacity to conduct military operations at a distance from its borders. In the mid-1960's, there were the first signs that the Soviets were attempting to develop this capability. The Soviets added two carriers to their fleet. These carriers have landing areas capable of handling helicopters and vertical takeoff aircraft. In addition, the Soviets have developed a force similar to the U.S. Marines. If the Soviets continue to expand their naval and amphibious forces, they will have the capability of continued probings in areas where U.S. interests are assumed to be less vital and not well defined, and where such probes would be unlikely to lead to nuclear confrontation. Under these circumstances, the Soviets might extend in a limited way their overseas defense commitments.

REGIONAL STRATEGIC INTERESTS

Overseas bases and narrow waters—Two general developments of the 1960's affected the overseas strategic position of the United States. Local political instabilities, coupled with the withdrawal of the British in the Far East, decreased substantially the number of overseas naval bases available to the United States. Secondly, the Soviet Union increased its presence in countries bordering on narrow and strategically important waters.

In conventional terms the most practical way of keeping strong military forces readily available is to use an overseas base. The adverse effects on the balance of payments through the heavy local cost of base maintenance was generally considered to be outweighed by the advantages of the local shore facility for supply and repair. Furthermore, technology was not available to provide economically a large floating support organization.

The political vulnerability of overseas bases is well illustrated by the situation with respect to the Seventh Fleet. The Seventh Fleet is the core of our military strength in the Western Pacific and the greatest naval force in the world. It is based at sea with support facilities largely at Yokosuka in Japan, Subic Bay in the Philippines, and in Hawaii and the West Coast. Land-based aircraft used in support of operations of the Seventh Fleet are maintained in Japan and Okinawa, as well as on our own western Pacific islands, such as Guam. The bases in Japan are part of a mutual defense agreement but there has been strong political opposition to the existence of these bases on Japanese soil, and in the future it may be expected that the United States will have to give up these bases. The Philippine situation is much more complex. The U.S. commitment to defend the Philippines against external aggression will no doubt continue, but the internal conditions look far less stable than those in Japan or even South Korea or Taiwan. The government during the 1960's was not effective in promoting the economy and there is evidence that the Communist Huk insurgency will rise again. Whether the United States can continue to maintain effective bases in such a politically unstable environment remains to be seen.

Similar basing problems affect ships of the Sixth Fleet which sails the Mediterranean and the Second Fleet in the Atlantic. The British have given up naval bases in Asia and the only important naval facility in either the South Atlantic or Indian Ocean is Simonstown, 30 miles from Capetown. During periods when the Suez Canal is closed, Simonstown is a particularly valuable base since it serves ships coming from the Atlantic to the Indian Ocean and to the waters off Southeast Asia. Simonstown thus assumes very great strategic importance. The apartheid policies followed by South Africa may lead to a substantial worsening of relations between that country and the United States and this, together with pressures from the United Nations, might result in an abandoning of Simonstown as a supporting base for U.S. naval forces.

Elsewhere, the great naval base at Trincomalee in Ceylon has deteriorated and its use in any crisis is unlikely. The Indian and Pakistan bases are also subject to continuing political uncertainty.

One alternative to overseas bases is the so-called fleet train or floating support which consists of ships and mobile floating docks which are used to repair and maintain warships, submarines, and aircraft and keep them supplied with food, stores, and provisions. During World War II, the British Pacific Fleet was serviced by a fleet train while today the American Sixth Fleet operates largely with the aid of a floating support organization. The principal arguments against such floating support units are that they are expensive and vulnerable.

The ultimate solution to overseas bases may lie in the construction of giant floating platforms that could be stationed against wind and current. A global array of such sites would protect areas of strategic interest, and would not be subject to the political uncertainties of land bases, which often are an international irritant. The technology for such floating platforms is closely tied to the technology of off-shore exploration and production; they both require buoyant supports extending well below the zone of wave action and though unsinkable would be vulnerable, as land bases are today, to air or missile strikes.

While the technological problems associated with such platforms are not insuperable, their emplacement would raise a host of difficult legal questions.

Traditional naval strategy has assigned great importance to the narrow waters of the world, those waters that occupy vital positions on shipping routes. These include Panama, Suez, the Straits of Gibraltar, Malaga, Sunda, and the Gulf of Aden. Apprehension that these narrow waters might be exploited during limited wars or times of crisis is heightened because at one time or another Soviet influence has been active in such countries as Algeria, Egypt, Syria, Somalia, Yemen, Cuba, and Indonesia—all situated close to the world's chief shipping bottlenecks. In particular, substantial amounts of Soviet military aid has gone to the United Arab Republic, Cuba and Indonesia. In addition to the danger that Soviet influence may lead these countries to undertake harassment, there is also the possibility that the countries bordering the narrow waters might attempt to exploit the vulnerabilities of the shipping routes. In this case, technology can provide a possible counter in the use of very large vessels, whereby the cost of alternative and much longer routes is not prohibitive. For example, the estimated cost for a 300,000 ton tanker delivering oil from Kuwait to western Europe is around $2.30/ton, while a tanker going through the Suez (less than 70,000 tons) delivers oil at about $1.00 more per ton. While in the near term, potential control of narrow waters will continue as an international irritant, it would appear likely that the strategic importance of such waters will decrease in the future as alternative routes become economical.

NATO—The NATO alliance was formed in 1949 because of the belief that the Soviet Union might attempt a military move in central Europe. Both the Berlin blockade in 1948 and the Korean War strengthened this feeling. During the 1950's and early 1960's the belief that war was imminent in Europe declined steadily. This decline was accompanied by a lessening dependence of the NATO countries on the United States for trade and a growing independence of the NATO nations' foreign policies.

Despite the general view of the lessening probability of war breaking out in Europe, several situations gave rise to crises and these may recur. For example, the Soviets on three occasions used East German forces to stop or interfere with Allied traffic going to West Berlin. Alternatively, another Hungarian-type situation could develop in the 1970's, where the economic and political ties of the United States and her NATO allies to the country involved are stronger than they were at the time of the Hungarian revolt. Or the Soviets may react to concerted moves on the part of West and East Germany at reunification.

In preparation for such eventualities the NATO alliance has prepared several strategies in which naval forces play different roles. In the massive retaliation strategy, ground troops serve the function of signalling that aggression has in fact taken place. Once such action has begun, the U.S. strategic offensive forces would be directed against the Soviet Union with the Polaris fleet either being held in reserve to knock out remaining Soviet forces or participating in the initial attack. The second strategy involves the use of tactical nuclear weapons in support of ground action. The weapons could be employed in several ways: as a warning, as a selective battlefield weapon, or as a general weapon. The war would be fought on the ground and sea forces would be used in a conventional role for supply, and submarine attacks on convoys would be expected. Such a situation is highly unstable as both sides would be tempted to escalate, with increasing numbers of tactical nuclear weapons used on land and on sea. Civilian populations could not be isolated and there would be strong pressures to bring the strategic forces into play. Finally, there is the strategy of the use of solely conventional forces with the expectation that in a prolonged war Europe would be supplied by sea. While perhaps more stable than the strategy of using tactical nuclear weapons, there would be the same pressures for escalation.

The forces of the NATO countries have been structured so that any one of the three options could be employed. In particular, the United States developed its Polaris fleet for deterrence but at the same time attempted to maintain substantial anti-submarine warfare capability. On the Soviet side, the defense planners have clearly taken into account the possibility of a protracted land war with the need for overseas supplies. The Soviets have built a large submarine fleet complemented by coastal defense missile boats.

Japan—In the decade between 1955 and 1965, Japan's economy surged with a growth rate of about 10 per cent per year, discounting the effects of inflation. Its gross national product has increased so that it is now greater than all the rest of geographic Asia, if India and China are excluded. U.S.–Japanese relations have become both intricate and rewarding. Trade between the United States and Japan passed the $5 billion mark in the mid-1960's. Japan ranks second only to Canada as a U.S. trading partner, and it is farther ahead in trade with the United States than any single European country. Because of Japan's strategic location, and because of this great economic interdependence, Japan is the most important non-European country to the United States.

Although Japan is widening her markets in the communist world, trade with Free World countries dominates and will into the 1970's.

In the mid 1960's, Japan achieved not only economic stability but also a substantial measure of political stability accompanied by a diminishing internal communist threat.

Japan's economic position is largely dependent on overseas trade. Japan's expenditures for national defense have been proportionately small, and of this little has been devoted to naval forces. The defense agreement of Japan and the United States is important not only to the actual defense of Japan but also to the problem of stability in East Asia and the security of sea lanes, both of which are vital to Japan. It would be in the U.S. interest for Japan to continue its defense agreements with the United States, but at the same time develop its own defense forces. For example, Japan has a sophisticated missile development program which could be rapidly turned to the purposes of self defense. The impressive shipbuilding industry developed by Japan could, in a relatively short time scale, provide Japan with a modern and capable naval force.

The United States can be expected to provide a nuclear shield for Japan against possible actions by China or even the Soviet Union. But it would appear to be in both Japanese and U.S. interests for Japan to develop the capability of militarily assisting the United States in maintaining stability within Asia. However achieving such a position, in which Japan partly rearmed herself, would take fundamental changes in the strong pacifist and neutralist sentiments that have developed since World War II.

In addition to the possibility of cooperating, with the United States, to maintain stability within Asia, Japan also has a great opportunity to contribute to the development of ocean resources. It has a sophisticated deep water fishing industry and has been one of the leaders in the development of methods of aquaculture. Exportation of these techniques and tools to the lesser developed countries in Asia could contribute significantly to stability in this part of the world.

Southeast Asia—SEATO was designed as an international answer to the problem of instability in Asia, but the developments in the 1960's show this effort to be a failure. The war in Vietnam, the divisions in Laos, and the political uncertainties of Cambodia all testify to this failure. The position of the United States is further complicated by bilateral commitments with Taiwan and the Philippines. These treaties have been taken by the rest of the world to mean that Southeast Asia is an American problem.

The Southeast Asian mainland presents us with great dangers and great problems. Continued instability in Vietnam and Laos can be expected. Thailand is a decidedly more stable country with a long history of both independence and dictatorship. Thailand as a whole is fairly prosperous and has been able to move ahead economically, but will continue to be under pressure by communist insurgents, particularly in the Northeast region. It can be expected that the Chinese will continue probes around their borders and, as was the case against India and in the Taiwan Straits, against the off-shore islands. In addition, Communist China can be expected to support wars of liberation within the Indonesian peninsula and perhaps throughout Southeast Asia. The extent to which the Chinese support such activities will depend on their nuclear capabilities. As the Chinese develop a nuclear deterrent which could be targeted against Asian cities, they may participate in a more active way and the United States may find itself in the position again of either withdrawing from a substantial section of Southeast Asia and leaving it under direct influence of China or undertaking another limited war effort.

Potentially the richest country in Southeast Asia is Indonesia. It sits astride the principal shipping routes from the Middle East to the Asian mainland and to Japan. Its economic development will, of course, depend greatly on political stability. After the replacement of the Sukarno government in the middle 1960's, Indonesia's trade was reoriented toward greater contacts with the West, although Indonesia maintained significant economic and military relationships with the Soviet Union.

Indonesia borders on very substantial continental shelf areas which probably contain rich oil and gas reserves and other minerals. Indonesia will not possess the capital or the technological capabilities to exploit these resources for a long time. Such exploitation might be undertaken in the meantime by American industry provided some sort of stability was achieved both in Indonesia and in Southeast Asia.

Iran—By the 1960's, Iran had reduced its dependence on the United States and improved its relationship with the Soviet Union. If this development becomes a trend and continues into the 1970's, the Soviet–Iranian relationship will assume a quite different complexion by 1975. The alignment of Iran with the Soviet Union would provide the Soviet Union with access to the oil-rich Persian Gulf and place the Soviet Union much closer to the Arabian Peninsula.

Arabian Peninsula—The withdrawal of the United Kingdom from the oil-rich Arabian Peninsula in the mid 1960's left a power vacuum in this region which can be expected to be a source of continuing competition for influence. The Soviet Union and the United States are joined in this competition with the United Arab Republic, with the latter strongly influenced by the Soviets. The Arabian Peninsula is of great importance to the Free World since it supplies a major fraction of the oil requirements of the NATO countries and Japan. This is likely to continue into the 1970's even with the development and accessibility of Libyan and Algerian oil fields. Lines of communication between oil sources and the Free World are highly vulnerable. Oil must move by ship through the Persian Gulf into Europe either through Suez, after passing by French Somaliland and Aden and Yemen or the long route around the Cape. Soviet influence is increasing both in Yemen and in Somaliland and the British abandoned Aden in 1968; if the Soviets were to occupy a naval base in Somaliland, their strategic position would be greatly enhanced.

The oil resources are presently held by small anti-communist oligarchies in countries with small populations, very large wealth and a weak military. The United Arab Republic, strengthened by Soviet arms, may very well attempt to gain control over one or more of these, perhaps along the pattern the United Arab Republic has followed in the Yemen conflict. Kuwait, Dhahran, and Qatar are all likely candidates for such attempts.

The Mediterranean and the Near East—The U.S. Sixth Fleet together with the fleets of the Allies has controlled the Mediterranean since World War II. This control has not prevented Soviet political and economic penetration in substantial areas of Arabia and Africa bordering the Mediterranean. Soviet interests in Algeria, Morocco, Egypt, Iraq, and Syria are substantial and long standing. But these countries did not welcome the Soviet military presence in the 1960's. Direct Soviet military activities in the Mediterranean have been restricted during these years to naval operations and visits to ports, principally Egyptian. The Soviet fleet in the Mediterranean suffers from Western control of the Dardanelles and Gibraltar. So far the Soviets have not been able to acquire a naval base in the Mediterranean, while the Sixth Fleet not only operates with its support afloat but also uses bases in Spain and Malta.

In the 1970's, there will be further opportunities for the Soviets to expand their political influence through military and economic aid programs to the Mediterranean, Africa, and to the countries of the Middle East as well by trade agreements. The continued presence of an American fleet could inhibit any direct Soviet military incursions in this area, but without the U.S. fleet the Allied fleets may not be sufficient to counter the United Arab Republic if, with great aid from the Soviet Union, it invades Israel or undertakes major military operations against oil-rich sheikdoms.

The Americas—All countries of Latin America have significant economic dependence on foreign trade and the United States is the chief trading partner of all these countries with the exception of Cuba. The United States and its allies depend on Latin America in varying degrees for numerous strategic materials, while Latin America imports a vast variety of industrial and manufacturing goods. Venezuela, with its large export of oil, is particularly important to the United States and to the NATO countries.

Cuba provides a focal point for Soviet activities in the Americas and may in the 1970's align herself more closely with China. It is quite hostile to continued U.S. military occupation of Guantanamo and may in the future permit the Soviets use of its territory for submarine support or surveillance activities. The principal concern to the United States is Cuba's support of communist-inspired indigenous insurgencies in Latin American countries or aggression by one Latin American country against another. Two countries of particular interest are Colombia and Venezuela, both of which are strategically located with respect to the approaches to the Panama Canal. Although the internal communist threat in both countries remained small in the 1960's, political instability could provide opportunity for a Cuban-supported revolution.

Use of Naval Forces

PROBLEMS OF LONG DEVELOPMENT TIMES OF WEAPONS SYSTEMS

In the modern world, operations at sea require ships containing equipment of vast technical complexity. The functions of command and control are aided by displays driven by computers. Weapons are delivered by largely automated fire control systems. Navigation and guidance of ships is done by computers and control systems of great complexity. This technological complexity was bought at a high cost. It provides that the vessel can undertake a variety of functions, but it also dictates that the time between conception of a weapons system and its deployment can be exceedingly long. A modern torpedo, for example, may have a research and development span of five to ten years and an integrated delivery system employing the torpedo may require even longer times.

Technical complexity with accompanying tactical flexibility assures in a sense a strategic rigidity. Because of costliness, elements of a naval force must be employed over a long time. All of this implies that political and international situations which dictated the mix of forces developed and deployed by a nation may change within a much shorter time than the time required for the navy to alter its force posture. For example, one may argue that the Soviets developed a large submarine fleet in the years following World War II because they expected to fight a major land war in central Europe and this fleet was designed to interdict supplies flowing from the United States to Europe. By the 1960's, the possibilities of war in central Europe had decreased very greatly but the Soviets still possessed a large conventionally powered submarine fleet with limited capabilities. The fleet cannot be scrapped out of hand until naval officers are convinced that they possess an adequate substitute. Symmetrically, the American navy developed with a main function of maintaining Europe during a general war.

Looking into the 1970's, it is quite clear that aside from a possible nuclear catastrophe, the major points of engagement of the United States and its possible competitors will be in Third World areas often far removed from adequately secured bases and in regions where conventional warfare cannot be practiced. The U.S. Navy of the future should be structured so that it can accomplish two principal missions, providing not only a strategic deterrent but also a deterrent to the spread of wars of liberation or subversion of Chinese and Soviet interests into areas where the interests of the United States are held important. On the other hand, the structure of the Soviet Navy will undoubtedly be designed to best achieve their policy objectives. These include convincing the United States of the credibility and adequacy of the Soviet nuclear strategic capability, and continuing to probe and expand in those areas where a direct clash of American interest is unlikely.

In 1968, the greatest naval power in the world was the United States. Its Navy comprised a worldwide commitment of men and ships requiring an operating budget on the order of $20 billion a year. The U.S. Navy had 145 submarines of which 41 were of the Polaris type. It had 300 destroyers, 15 attack carriers and 17 helicopter and support carriers. By comparison the Soviet Navy was much smaller. It consisted of two helicopter carriers, 19 cruisers, 170 frigates and destroyer escorts, 55 nuclear powered submarines, and 305 other submarines. The Soviet Navy also contained a large number, about 560, of small torpedo and missile boats. The other navies of the world were small by comparison. Both France and the United Kingdom had two attack carriers and a relatively small number of destroyers and frigates. The conventional submarine forces of these two countries were very much smaller than those of either the United States or the Soviet Union.

In assessing possible naval capabilities of the Soviet Union and the United States in the 1970's, it should be remembered that technology, even though slow moving, can bring about very great changes. For example, it is imaginable that a nation could control the surface of the oceans without having a single ship. The required system would involve satellites equipped with a variety of sensors that would maintain coverage of the world's oceans. Satellites would relay the information to a central computer system which would then target the land-based missiles on ships to be destroyed. The missiles would then be equipped with terminal guidance or be under direct control of the satellite and land-based computer systems. While it is most unlikely that any nation would adopt such a strategy, this example illustrates the fact that naval posture may change radically in the future.

DETERRENT ROLE OF THE NAVY

Development of long-range ballistic missiles in the 1950's caused a revolution in the method of waging strategic warfare. Starting in late 1953, the United States engaged in an urgent program to build up its ballistic missile forces. The Soviet Union embarked on the same kind of program even earlier. Missiles were originally contemplated as fixed devices on land. At roughly the same time, however, the U.S. Navy undertook a program to develop a nuclear submarine, and mounted a concerted and highly inventive weapons systems development program to adapt ballistic missiles to it. The system, named Polaris, consists of a small solid rocket ballistic missile launchable from a submerged nuclear submarine. Polaris, with a high degree of invulnerability, has become a fundamental building block for the U.S. strategic forces. Indeed, a thought often expressed at the time was that the ultimate nuclear stability would have both the Soviet Union and the United States equipped only with invulnerable Polaris forces and that neither side would have a ballistic missile defense for population centers. In that way, the outcome of a nuclear exchange would be clear and unmistakable and the possibility of a first nuclear strike, even in critical times, would be minimized. (This concept of deterrence through assured vulnerability, however, provided no protection against the possibility of accidental war; nor can it protect against what may in the 1970's become the problem of the unidentifiable assailant.)

The effectiveness of a submarine-based missile force is highly contingent on concealment, dispersion, high mobility, and very long patrol times. A major technical uncertainty is whether or not some means for detecting underwater submarines quickly and at long range will be developed. At present, detection is based on sound; either the sound generated by the submarine or the sound sent out by a hunter of submarines and reflected back by the quarry. The complicated sound characteristics of the oceans and of the ocean bottom make detection difficult, particularly at long distances. In addition, submarines can be quieted so that they radiate relatively low amounts of noise, making their detection even more difficult. However, submarines may give off tell-tale signals of other kinds not yet recognized that would give them away. Some aspect of the ocean environment conceivably could be exploited or utilized to allow continuous targeting of submarines. If Polaris submarines could be continuously targeted, they would be open to preemptive attack by ballistic missiles with relatively large warheads.

As enemy missile accuracy improves and as enemy missile payloads become more sophisticated, concealment and mobility become relatively more important. Because the United States has become increasingly concerned with penetrating Soviet ballistic missile defenses, larger and more sophisticated payloads for U.S. strategic forces have become increasingly important. The development of the Poseidon undersea launching system provided a significant improvement in our strategic capability in this regard. However, the United States can look forward to the need for even greater strategic capabilities in the future. Moreover, a submarine-based missile force has some less than ideal characteristics. It is relatively expensive to operate compared to land missile forces and it is presently limited in the size of the warhead it can deliver. Consequently, the ocean-based missile force of the future could conceivably take some totally new direction of development which would combine many of the better characteristics of the land-based force: less expensive, larger payloads, better command and control, with some characteristics of the submarine force invulnerability. This does not imply that the United States will not also have an interest in developing missile-carrying submarines capable of operating at much greater depths. It may be that the ocean bottom topography would help conceal their presence and make them even less susceptible to enemy counteraction.

Such developments may, for example, take the form of placing missiles as large or even larger than Polaris size on relatively shallow underwater barge systems on the continental shelf in such a way as to conceal their location. The underwater barges would move infrequently so that the potential of their being tracked by motion-generated noise would be minimized. Another possibility would be a slightly mobile ocean bottom system which creeps along. Systems of this kind, of course, will require different kinds of marine engineering from that which produced the current submarine-based force. Such systems can involve much larger missiles, might require underwater maintenance by personnel also located underwater, might entail development of new kinds of detection and survival equipment to prevent attacks and emplacements, and so on. Such systems would also raise very substantial legal and political questions about whether or not nations have the right either to use the continental shelf to emplace offensive strategic systems or to use portions of the ocean bottom in the interest of national defense.

The Soviet Union has relied less on submarines for its nuclear deterrent. It does have a large number of submarines capable of firing cruise (air breathing) rather than ballistic missiles. Such submarines would have a role in attacks against other naval forces or attacks against NATO countries. The Soviets have not exploited to any great degree submarine-based ballistic missiles for two principal reasons. Russian submarines must traverse great expanses of water which are under surveillance by the United States and its allies. There is no guarantee that the submarines could proceed to station without detection. Furthermore, the Soviets probably judged that land-based missiles are much more economical for a given delivered megatonnage than the all-out investment required for a Polaris-type system. It would appear that the Soviets have chosen to provide security to their offensive forces both by developing anti-ballistic missile defenses and by mobile land basing.

Britain and France both decided in the 1960's to build a small submarine missile force, since the relative invulnerability of such a force makes it well suited for nations which by restriction on resources and on territory cannot deploy large numbers of land-based missiles.

In summary, the United States will almost certainly depend upon submarine-launched missiles as an important part of its strategic deterrent. The Soviet Union will probably maintain a small submarine component, but not rely upon it in any major way. In the 1970's and beyond, it is possible that the kind of strategic offensive force the United States may wish to develop will rely even more heavily on ocean-based systems than has been the case up to now. Such systems will require operations at a much wider range of ocean environment and over a much longer time than present. Operations in greater depths will aid in concealment while greater geographic coverage will make continuous tracking and targeting much more difficult.

NAVY'S ROLE IN GENERAL WAR

The structures of both the U.S. and the Soviet navies have been influenced by considerations of a general land war in Europe. The war has been thought of as either being limited to the use of conventional weapons or including the use of tactical nuclear weapons. The Soviet Navy has built up a very substantial submarine force to undertake interdiction and has built over 500 torpedo and missile carrying boats to provide for its coastal defense. Thus the Soviet Navy through the early 1960's was thought of primarily as a defensive force and an auxiliary to the land army. As late as 1965, the Chief of the Soviet general staff, Marshall Zakharof, spoke of "cherishing the defense capabilities of our country and our Red Army as the apple of our eye."

In turn the U.S. Navy has emphasized its anti-submarine warfare program, which is charged with the mission of developing a capability to destroy enemy submarine forces. In support of the ASW role, the Navy put together a variety of systems with ASW capability. These include attack submarines, anti-submarine carrier groups, long-range patrol aircraft, and sophisticated listening devices.

According to conventional naval strategists these two forces would be joined during a protracted land war in Europe. However, the broader strategic considerations discussed earlier make it seem most unlikely that there would ever be a lengthy land engagement. Nuclear weapons would certainly be brought into play at an early stage and there would be strong pressures on both sides to escalate to strategic missiles. Once a full scale nuclear war had begun there would be no appreciable role for naval forces. Both sides would take vast destruction and ports would not have the capability of loading supplies and even if supplies could be unloaded there would be no transportation system available to distribute the supplies inland. Control of the sea under these circumstances would be a meaningless exercise. Naval forces might participate in emergency rescue and relief operations but it is impossible to imagine a protracted war at sea under conditions of a general nuclear exchange.

WARS OF LIBERATION

In general, the spokesmen for modern communist expansionism agree that nuclear war is a disaster which must be avoided at all costs and that furthermore even conventional non-nuclear war is too dangerous for indulgence, since such wars may escalate into nuclear wars. Thus it is subversive warfare, the war of "national liberation," which by tunneling under the conventional defenses of the non-communist state offers the most favorable possibilities for a communist take-over. Being cheap, disavowable, and relatively free from risk, this method may be the preferred course of action, particularly in those areas of the world where the U.S. interest is low. On the other hand, the U.S. view at least up to Vietnam only partially paralleled that of the Soviets. The United States in the 1960's rejected nuclear war but viewed limited war as a form of military force which might be used in the national interest under certain circumstances. However, events in Vietnam led to a reexamination of this latter point. For example, in 1967, the Senate Armed Services Committee declined to authorize funds for Fast Deployment Logistic ships on the grounds that fast deployment capability would encourage further interventions on the Vietnam pattern.

For countries bordering on communist nations, naval power can provide little or no deterrent to the external support of insurgencies and limited guerrilla activities. Naval forces can come into play only when the political decision has been made to use U.S. forces either in the air or on the ground. Support might first take the form of air cover for government forces. In this situation, carriers could play a critical role, particularly if the situation develops rapidly and there are inadequate provisions on the ground for secure land-based aircraft. Indeed the argument can be made that the war in Vietnam escalated as a result of deploying land-based aircraft in South Vietnam, since this deployment was followed by the need to protect these bases with American ground troops. Once ground troops were introduced they entered into action and began the spiraling escalation. Such ground involvement might be avoided through the use of carriers providing both fixed-wing and helicopter support to local forces. The carriers would have to be protected particularly against missile attacks launched from small boats, which have been widely distributed among lesser developed nations by the Soviet Union. A further mission of carrier-based aircraft would be to provide air reconnaissance for the detection and surveillance of guerrilla units, thus further enhancing the capability of the local forces.

Once the decision is made to deploy ground forces, naval forces are essential to support amphibious and airborne assault landings. The principal characteristic that naval forces used in support of actions against wars of liberation must possess if they are to be effective is that of speed of reaction. Although guerrilla activities may extend over a long time, critical situations arise where traditional air power supporting government troops may tip the balance.

Naval forces may be able to play a new and important role as a deterrent to the overseas encouragement of indigenous communist efforts. The presence of the American fleet in the Pacific lessens the likelihood that China will support a communist movement in either the Philippines or Indonesia, although the fleet does not completely remove that possibility. The continuing presence of naval forces in a given area of the world could discourage open assistance to guerrilla forces, though overt action on the high seas against the forces of a great power may be precluded by the risk of escalation.

CONCEPT OF WAR AT SEA

The nuclear stalemate and the unlikelihood of war in Europe has raised in some minds the speculation that a considerable war might be conducted wholly at sea with the land remaining a sanctuary. The U.S. Navy has devoted considerable attention to this concept in recent years. A typical scenario envisaged in war at sea would be the Free World's response at sea to a new Soviet action against West Berlin. The response would take place at sea either in the form of harassment of Soviet shipping or some countering blockade. The exploitation of a war at sea option is of potential interest to sea powers. The option is particularly attractive to those sea powers which have the capability of employing their naval forces against opponent countries which are significantly dependent upon the use of the sea. When these conditions are obtained, war at sea has two potential virtues. The first is that because of the freedom of the seas military forces could take positions so as to constitute a threat of coercive military action without invading the opponent's territory or opening fire on the opponent. The exercise of the war at sea option might accomplish its purpose without seizure of territory or even without hostilities. The second virtue is that if hostilities did occur and they were confined to the sea, civilian and military casualties would be held at a minimum.

Objections can be raised against the value of exercising the war at sea options. First, although one of the apparent virtues to the option of war at sea is freedom of the seas, the sea option, when exercised, will be an encroachment on that freedom. Thus, there is a risk of arousing the opposition of some, if not all, maritime powers who use the sea. Second, there is the danger of escalation not only to land warfare but to nuclear conflict.

In some ways, the war at sea option does not appear attractive either to the United States or to the Soviet Union. The United States is more heavily dependent on foreign trade than is the Soviet Union and certain of its allies, particularly Japan and the United Kingdom, are very much more so. These countries are particularly vulnerable to any response the Soviet Union might make to an initial exercise of the option by the United States. To the Soviet Union, the option is not attractive because of the overwhelming superiority of U.S. naval forces. Perhaps because of this, there has been little consideration of war at sea options in the strategic writings in the Soviet Union.

ROLE OF NAVAL FORCES IN INTELLIGENCE

In the 1960's the use of the seas for gathering intelligence both by naval vessels and by supporting vessels, such as the ubiquitous Russian trawler fleet, greatly increased. These activities were not confined solely to gathering information about the opponent's naval forces and their technical characteristics but also included gathering intelligence on shore installations, missile firing and space shots. In a sense these activities provided vital data to the defense planners of the opponent's capabilities and served a stabilizing role. But because of their great vulnerability and the covert nature of their operation, they also led to serious international incidents, as was illustrated by the Israeli attack upon the U.S.S. Liberty during the Arab-Israeli war of 1967 and the North Korean capture of the U.S.S. Pueblo in 1968.

As long as intelligence ships are unescorted and unarmed, they are a tempting target because of the sophisticated electronic equipment they contain, as well as the political leverage that can be exercised if they are captured. Escorting these vessels decreases their covertness and in this way lessens the chance of gathering significant intelligence, while it is unlikely that they can be sufficiently armed to deter a persistent opponent.

SUMMARY COMMENTS ON THE STRUCTURE OF U.S. NAVAL FORCES

In the 1960's, the structure of the U.S. Navy was heavily influenced by consideration of the possibility of a land war in Europe. This led to heavy emphasis on anti-submarine warfare capabilities, both on the surface and beneath the surface. The ability of the Navy to support amphibious or land operations overseas, although substantially greater than that of any other power, still falls short of the requirements for the 1970's. It would appear that greater emphasis should be placed on carriers integrated with their support units which are able to move rapidly and provide support to actions on land through helicopters, vertical take off and landing aircraft (VTOL), and conventional fixed-wing aircraft.

The continuing need for a nuclear deterrent will require that the Navy maintain an undersea force capable of launching ballistic missiles. Whether this force should be a relatively shallow-based submarine system, such as Poseidon, or a deeper-running and slower vehicle possessing longer-range missiles is a question for detailed analysis.

Goals for a National Ocean Program

Determination of goals for a national ocean program in the 1970's must, of course, be based on the marine interests of the United States. These interests are threefold: social, economic, and strategic. Science and technology support all three concerns.

Technological advances of the recent past and the near future force a new view of the oceans. First of all, an advancing deep-sea technology will permit the exploration of the third dimension of the ocean—an exploration that has only barely begun.

Technological developments permit operations in parts of the ocean, both on the bottom and throughout the ocean levels immediately above bottom-mounted installations. There may be teams of men working at these installations at all depths. We cannot foresee all the legal problems but we can tell that these massive investments have a value that make them attractive military targets, a possible source of international blackmail and friction, and in general a central concern of those involved in planning for naval forces.

Space and computer technology provide highly industrialized nations, such as the Soviet Union and the United States, with the capability of maintaining surveillance over major activities on the surface of the ocean. Developments in both science and technology make it appear possible that if a nation so desired, it could maintain constant surveillance of major ocean-going vessels sometime in the 1970's. Structuring of naval forces of operations "in the open" presents the defense planners with a great variety of problems qualitatively different from those faced by naval strategists in the past.

Technology will provide means for new uses of the oceans. For high-cost cargo, long-range transport aircraft will compete with high speed ocean transports. An especially intriguing possibility is the development of means of chemically producing protein. Such protein may make unnecessary large scale development of the world's fishing fleets which otherwise would be required to deal with the protein deficiencies of the lesser developed nations.

Many of the activities of marine technology border on those of marine science. The marine science interests of the United States, which are shared by scientists around the world, involve observation, description, and understanding of physical, chemical, and biological phenomena of the marine environment. Once adequately served by conventional oceanography, today marine science converges with meteorology and solid earth geophysics. This unity of the marine sciences with other aspects of the environmental sciences presages a similar convergence of interest in the maintenance of atmospheric, oceanic, land, and air resources.

The economic interests of the United States in the oceans have been advanced greatly by scientific and technological progress. In the years prior to World War II, the United States was principally interested in the oceans as a means for long distance shipping and, to a limited but important extent, for food and recreation. Economic interests have been extended to include mineral resources, particularly oil and gas, from the continental shelf. As on land, complex interacting factors affect the profitability of efforts to exploit the sea's resources: access to market, legal ownership of resources, availability of relevant technology and capital, strength of competition, safety of operations, and inadvertent, uncontrolled interference from other human activities, such as waste disposal or warfare. Despite many uncertainties, developments in technology indicate that American industry may soon make profitable advances into the marine environment.

Strategic marine interests of the United States have both military and non-military aspects which are, of course, interdependent. The military aspects have had a long and complex history, but new technological and political developments, as reviewed above, make conventional naval strategy less relevant. The non-military aspects of the U.S. interest in the seas are even less well known. The new importance of peaceful uses of the ocean stems from a number of developments of the 1960's.

The deployment of nuclear weapons has led to a decreasing likelihood of direct military confrontation between the United States and the Soviet Union over territorial disputes because of the unacceptable risk of annihilation. This development strongly suggests that where there is competition for the acquisition of the ocean's resources, such as fish, minerals, or even the right of passage, in most instances such non-military factors as prior presence or continued use will be decisive in determining the outcome.

Along with the evolution of a nuclear balance of power, there has been a partial breakup of the Sino-Soviet bloc. This breakup means that Moscow and Peking must compete for leadership in the Communist world and in this competition both China and Russia will turn increasingly toward countries of the Third World. The growing interest of Moscow and Peking in lesser developed countries may lead to a direct confrontation with the United States. In some cases the fiercely competitive interests of the Communist countries and the Free World can lead to limited conflicts, as in Vietnam. In other areas, competition will involve both trade with Third World countries and aid in development of their ocean resources. Competitive advantage will go to those nations which have prepared themselves for this kind of confrontation.

In addition to the increasing Soviet interest in countries distant from Soviet borders, two political and economic developments will influence the United States strategy for the sea: the first of these is the precipitant withdrawal of British influence from major portions of the Far East and the Indian Ocean; the second is the remarkable economic development of Japan and the dependence of Japan's economy on overseas trade.

Of great strategic concern is the increasing worldwide importance of bringing population and food supply into balance especially in the less developed nations, and the possibility of a major breakdown of the world food economy within perhaps twenty years. Increased production of marine food resources for the less developed nations transcends mere economic considerations. Food from the sea offers at least a temporary and local relief from the exhausting efforts to feed increasing populations. The U.S. interest in these efforts is not only humanitarian but also national because of the worldwide political and social instability which might be expected as a consequence of any major food crisis. The strategic importance of food resources suggests one important focus for the U.S. program for the oceans in the 1970's.

Since social, economic, and strategic marine interests are interwoven and rapidly evolving in a context which includes similarly developing marine interests of other nations, a national ocean program is required which should have as its ultimate objective the effective use of the sea for all the purposes to which we now put the terrestrial environment: commerce, industry, recreation, settlement, and aid to security. The objective of an effective use of the sea implies that the long-term specific goals of U.S. policy for the sea should be:

1. To use the sea to stabilize world order by providing for food and other natural resources, by preserving the seas as a source of recreation, and by using the seas to mount cooperative ventures with truly international objectives;
2. To promote the economic interest of the United States by providing the means and safeguards to profitable investments;
3. To use the seas in ways designed to maintain a nuclear deterrent;
4. To provide the capability of effectively deterring any Sino-Soviet attempts at enlarging their spheres of influence by subversion or wars of liberation.

In support of these goals, further scientific and technical investigations designed to describe and understand marine phenomena, processes and resources should be carried out with the aim of acquiring the ability to predict, and ultimately to control phenomena affecting the safety and economy of sea-going activities. Furthermore, such investigations will be required to achieve the fullest exploitation of resources in and under the sea, and to provide the technical information requisite for both a nuclear deterrent and a deterrent to the use of the sea for the support of wars of liberation.

The effective use of the sea to further U.S. interests does not mean the abridgment or infringement of other nations' rights or interests. In fact, the oceans are so huge and potential benefits so great that a cooperative international effort to develop marine resources for the benefit of all humanity seems both logical and appealing. The institutional means for this development, however, are so rudimentary and activities and interests of other nations are evolving so fast that urgent and continuing U.S. efforts are required in the interim to preclude a possible abridgment of our interests by others.

The implication is that freedom of the seas cannot be conceived of as being static, especially since increasing intensity and sophistication of ocean exploitation require legal arrangements beyond the traditional understanding of this concept. An evolving concept of freedom of the seas does not imply that more suitable versions must reflect narrow conceptions of our national interests. The problem is to adapt the principle of freedom to the general interest rather than to any exclusive interest of our own. However, a realistic conception of freedom of the seas is likely to remain vital to protection of the marine interests of the United States.

Index

The American Assembly

The American Assembly holds meetings of national leaders and publishes books to illuminate issues of United States policy. The Assembly is a national, non-partisan educational institution, incorporated in the State of New York.

The Trustees of the Assembly approve a topic for presentation in a background book, authoritatively designed and written to aid deliberations at national Assembly sessions at Arden House, the Harriman (N.Y.) Campus of Columbia University. These books are also used to support discussion at regional Assembly sessions and to evoke considerations by the general public.

All sessions of the Assembly, whether international, national, or local, issue and publicize independent reports of conclusions and recommendations on the topic at hand. Participants in these sessions constitute a wide range of experience and competence.

American Assembly books are purchased and put to use by thousands of individuals, libraries, businesses, public agencies, nongovernmental organizations, educational institutions, discussion meetings, and service groups.

The subjects of Assembly studies to date are:

1951———United States–Western Europe Relationships
1952———Inflation
1953———Economic Security for Americans
1954———The United States Stake in the United Nations
———The Federal Government Service
1955———United States Agriculture
———The Forty-Eight States
1956———The Representation of the United States Abroad
———The United States and the Far East
1957———International Stability and Progress
———Atoms for Power
1958———The United States and Africa
———United States Monetary Policy
1959———Wages, Prices, Profits, and Productivity
———The United States and Latin America
1960———The Federal Government and Higher Education
———The Secretary of State
———Goals for Americans
1961———Arms Control: Issues for the Public
———Outer Space: Prospects for Man and Society
1962———Automation and Technological Change
———Cultural Affairs and Foreign Relations

1963———The Population Dilemma
———The United States and the Middle East
1964———The United States and Canada
———The Congress and America's Future
1965———The Courts, the Public and the Law Explosion
———The United States and Japan
1966———The United States and the Philippines
———State Legislatures in American Politics
———A World of Nuclear Powers?
———Population Dilemma in Latin America
———Challenges to Collective Bargaining
1967———The United States and Eastern Europe
———Ombudsmen for American Government?
1968———Uses of the Seas
———Law in a Changing America
———World Hunger

Second Editions:

1962———The United States and the Far East
1963———The United States and Latin America
———The United States and Africa
1964———United States Monetary Policy
1965———The Federal Government Service
———The Representation of the United States Abroad
1967———The United States and the Middle East
1968———Outer Space: Prospects for Man and Society
———Cultural Affairs and Foreign Relations